KING ARTHUR AND HIS KNIGHTS

BY
MARY
MACLEOD

ILLUSTRATED
BY
HOWARD PYLE

PARENTS' MAGAZINE PRESS
A Division of Parents' Magazine Enterprises, Inc.
New York

PREFACE

Lost from all view in the deep mists of the past, the origin of these stories about King Arthur will never be uncovered. The first-known of them have been traced as far back as the sixth century. Possibly in that remote age there existed some noble Briton whose acts became legends, told and retold to children. Generation after generation of storytellers heard bits of the tales in many parts of Europe, and filled in the gaps according to their own ideas. We know that by the year 1100, Arthurian legends were familiar in Italy and beyond; drifting widely from their English birthplace and changing, of course, as they spread. They belong to mythology, not to history.

Sir Thomas Malory is the name that dominates this area of our literature. He gathered different versions of the stories, pieced together their fragments, and unified the whole work, for all time, in his *Morte d'Arthur*. It was the first epic written in English prose. William Caxton printed the twenty-one volumes in 1485, fourteen years after Malory's death. Britain previously had known these Celtic flavored myths in the country's traditional poetry. They exalted the ideals of medieval chivalry and kept them aloft.

Mary Macleod's simple, direct version, as chosen for this volume, is based on Malory, and remains a standard in its own right. It was first published in 1900.

The ancient tales relate that Arthur was a king above reproach, and the gentlest, most honorable knight who ever lived. To his Round Table at Camelot belonged a worthy company of heroes, among them Lancelot, the bravest knight, Tristram, who loved Iseult, Sir Gareth, and the purest knight of them all, Galahad, son of Lancelot and Elaine.

Students of Celtic mythology agree on no exact location for Camelot, where Arthur held his court, and brought Guinevere as his bride. Sometimes the old seat of the Round Table is identified with the village of Camelford, in Cornwall near Tintagel. One legend says that on a future day Arthur will come again to rule over England and save his people; that on his tomb it was written, "Here lies Arthur, King that was, and King that shall be."

Arthur and his knights of the Round Table righted the wrongs they encountered. Their splendid deeds led finally to the quest for the Holy Grail. Our western world's heritage of literature and music has drawn inspiration from this chivalrous realm, which belongs to all young readers today.

IRENE SMITH
Former Superintendent of Work with Children
Brooklyn Public Library
Brooklyn, New York

CONTENTS

THE BOY OF THE KITCHEN

THE FOREST KNIGHT

KING FOX

THE QUEST OF THE HOLY GRAIL

THE DEATH OF ARTHUR

KING ARTHUR

THE MARVEL OF THE SWORD

WHEN Uther Pendragon, King of England, died, the country for a long while stood in great danger, for every lord that was mighty gathered his forces, and many wished to be King. For King Uther's own son, Prince Arthur, who should have succeeded him, was but a child, and Merlin, the mighty magician, had hidden him away.

Now a strange thing had happened at Arthur's birth, and this was how it was.

Some time before Merlin had done Uther a great service, on condition that the King should grant him whatever he wished for. This the King swore a solemn oath to do. Then Merlin made him promise that when his child was born it should be delivered to Merlin to bring up as he chose, for this would be to the child's own great advantage. The King had given his promise so he was obliged to agree. Then Merlin said he knew a very true and faithful man, one of King Uther's lords, by name of Sir Ector, who had large possessions in many parts of England and Wales, and that the child should be given to him to bring up.

On the night the baby was born, while it was still unchristened, King Uther commanded two knights and two ladies to take it, wrapped in a cloth of gold, and deliver it to a poor man whom they would find waiting at the postern gate of the Castle. This poor man was Merlin in disguise, although they did not know it. So the child was delivered unto Merlin and he carried him to Sir Ector, and made a holy man christen him, and name him Arthur; and Sir Ector's wife cherished him as her own child.

Within two years King Uther fell sick of a great malady, and for three days and three nights he was speechless. All the Barons were in much sorrow, and asked Merlin what was best to be done.

"There is no remedy," said Merlin, "God will have His Will. But look ye all, Barons, come before King Uther tomorrow, and God will make him speak."

So the next day Merlin and all the Barons came before the King, and Merlin said aloud to King Uther:

"Sir, after your days shall your son Arthur be King of this realm and all that belongs to it?"

Then Uther Pendragon turned to him and said in hearing of them all:

"I give my son Arthur God's blessing and mine, and bid him pray for my soul, and righteously and honorably claim the Crown, on forfeiture of my blessing."

And with that, King Uther died.

But Arthur was still only a baby, not two years old, and Merlin knew it would be no use yet to proclaim him King. For there were many powerful nobles in England in those days, who were all trying to get the kingdom for themselves, and perhaps they would kill the little Prince. So there was much strife and debate in the land for a long time.

When several years had passed, Merlin went to the Archbishop of Canterbury and counselled him to send for all the lords of the realm, and all the gentlemen of arms, that they should come to London at Christmas, and for this cause— that a miracle would show who should be rightly King of the realm. So all the lords and gentlemen made themselves ready, and came to London, and long before dawn on Christmas Day they were all gathered in the great church of St. Paul's to pray.

When the first service was over, there was seen in the churchyard a large stone, four-square, like marble, and in the midst of it was like an anvil of steel, a foot high. In this was stuck by the point a beautiful sword, with naked blade, and there were letters written in gold about the sword, which said thus:

"Whoso pulleth this sword out of this stone and anvil is rightly King of all England."

Then the people marvelled, and told it to the Archbishop.

"I command," said the Archbishop, "that you keep within the church, and pray unto God still; and that no man touch the sword till the service is over."

So when the prayers in church were over, all the lords went to behold the stone and the sword; and when they read the writing some of them—such as wished to be King— tried to pull the sword out of the anvil. But not one could make it stir.

"The man is not here, that shall achieve the sword," said the Archbishop, "but doubt not God will make him known. But let us provide ten knights, men of good fame, to keep guard over the sword."

So it was ordained, and proclamation was made that every one who wished might try to win the sword. And upon New Year's Day the Barons arranged to have a great tournament, in which all knights who would joust or tourney might take a part. This was ordained to keep together the Lords and Commons, for the Archbishop trusted that it would be made known who should win the sword.

HOW ARTHUR WAS CROWNED KING

On New Year's Day, after church, the Barons rode to the field, some to joust, and some to tourney, and so it happened that Sir Ector, who had large estates near London, came also to the tournament; and with him rode Sir Kay, his son, with young Arthur, his foster brother.

As they rode, Sir Kay found he had lost his sword, for he had left it at his father's lodging, so he begged young Arthur to go and fetch it for him.

"That will I, gladly," said Arthur, and he rode fast away.

But when he came to the house, he found no one at home to give him the sword, for everyone had gone to see the jousting. Then Arthur was angry and said to himself:

"I will ride to the churchyard, and take the sword with me that sticketh in the stone, for my brother, Sir Kay, shall not be without a sword this day."

When he came to the churchyard he alighted, and tied his horse to the stile, and went to the tent. But he found there no knights, who should have been guarding the sword, for they were all away at the joust. Seizing the sword by the handle he lightly and fiercely pulled it out of the stone, then took his horse and rode his way, till he came to Sir Kay his brother, to whom he delivered the sword.

As soon as Sir Kay saw it, he knew well it was the sword of the Stone, so he rode to his father, Sir Ector, and said:

"Sir, lo, here is the sword to the Stone, wherefore I must be King of this land."

When Sir Ector saw the sword he turned back, and came to the church, and there they all three alighted and went into the church, and he made his son swear truly how he got the sword.

"By my brother Arthur," said Sir Kay, "for he brought it to me."

"How did you get this sword?" said Sir Ector to Arthur.

And the boy told him.

"Now," said Sir Ector, "I understand you must be King of this land."

"Wherefore I?" said Arthur; "and for what cause?"

"Sir," said Ector, "because God will have it so; for never man could draw out this sword but he that shall rightly be King. Now let me see whether you can put the sword there as it was, and pull it out again."

"There is no difficulty," said Arthur, and he put it back into the stone.

Then Sir Ector tried to pull out the sword, and failed; and Sir Kay also pulled with all his might, but it would not move.

"Now you shall try," said Sir Ector to Arthur.

"I will, well," said Arthur, and pulled the sword out easily.

At this Sir Ector and Sir Kay knelt down on the ground before him.

"Alas," said Arthur, "mine own dear father and brother, why do you kneel to me?"

"Nay, nay, my lord Arthur, it is not so; I was never your father, nor of your blood; but I know well you are of higher blood than I thought you were."

Then Sir Ector told him all, how he had taken him to bring up, and by whose command; and how he had received him from Merlin. And when he understood that Ector was not his father, Arthur was deeply grieved.

"Will you be my good, gracious lord, when you are King?" asked the knight.

"If not, I should be to blame," said Arthur, "for you are the man in the world to whom I am the most beholden and my good lady and mother your wife, who has fostered and kept me as well as her own children. And if ever it be God's will that I be King, as you say, you shall desire of me what I shall do, and I shall not fail you; God forbid I should fail you."

"Sir," said Sir Ector, "I will ask no more of you but that you will make my son, your foster brother Sir Kay, steward of all your lands."

"That shall be done," said Arthur, "and by my faith, never man but he shall have that office while he and I live."

Then they went to the Archbishop and told him how the sword was achieved, and by whom.

On Twelfth Day all the Barons came to the Stone in the churchyard, so that any who wished might try to win the sword. But not one of them all could take it out, except Arthur. Many of them therefore were very angry, and said it was a great shame to them and to the country to be governed by a boy not of high blood, for as yet none of them knew that he was the son of King Uther Pendragon. So they agreed to delay the decision till Candlemas, which is the second day of February.

But when Candlemas came, and Arthur once more was the only one who could pull out the sword, they put it off till Easter; and when Easter came, and Arthur again prevailed

7

in presence of them all, they put it off till the Feast of Pentecost.

Then by Merlin's advice the Archbishop summoned some of the best knights that were to be got—such knights as in his own day King Uther Pendragon had best loved and trusted most—and these were appointed to attend young Arthur, and never to leave him night or day till the Feast of Pentecost.

When the great day came, all manner of men once more made the attempt, and once more not one of them all could prevail but Arthur. Before all the Lords and Commons there assembled he pulled out the sword, whereupon all the Commons cried out at once:

"We will have Arthur for our King! We will put him no more in delay, for we all see that it is God's will that he shall be our King, and he who holdeth against it, we will slay him."

And therewith they knelt down all at once, both rich and poor, and besought pardon of Arthur, because they had delayed him so long.

And Arthur forgave them, and took the sword in both his hands, and offered it on the altar where the Archbishop was, and so he was made knight by the best man there.

After that, he was crowned at once, and there he swore to his Lords and Commons to be a true King, and to govern with true justice from thenceforth all the days of his life.

THE SIEGE OF THE STRONG TOWER

AFTER Arthur was crowned King many complaints were made to him of great wrongs that had been done since the death of King Uther; many Lords, Knights, Ladies and Gentlemen having been deprived of their lands. Thereupon King Arthur caused the lands to be given again to them that owned them. When this was done, and all the districts around London were settled, he made Sir Kay Steward of England, Sir Baldwin Constable of Britain, and Sir Ulfius, Chamberlain; while Sir Brastias was appointed Warden of the country north of the Trent. Most of this land was then held by the King's enemies, but within a few years Arthur had won all the north.

Some parts of Wales still stood out against him, but in due time he overcame them all, as he did the rest, by the noble prowess of himself, and the Knights of the Round Table.

Then King Arthur went into Wales, and proclaimed a great feast, to be held at Pentecost, after his crowning in the city of Carleon. To this feast came many rich and powerful Kings, with great retinues of knights. Arthur was glad of their coming, for he thought that the kings and knights had come in love, and to do him honor at his feast, wherefore he rejoiced greatly, and sent them rich presents.

The Kings, however, would receive none of them, but rebuked the messengers shamefully, saying it gave them no pleasure to receive gifts from a beardless boy of low blood. They sent him word that they would have none of his gifts, but they would come and give him gifts with hard swords betwixt the neck and the shoulders. It was for that they came hither, so they told the messengers plainly, for it was a great shame to them all to see a boy have the rule of so noble a realm as this land.

When the messengers brought this answer to King Arthur, by the advice of his Barons he betook himself with five hundred good men to a strong tower. And all the Kings laid siege to him, but King Arthur had plenty of food.

Within fifteen days Merlin, the great magician, came into the city of Carleon. All the Kings were very glad to see him, and asked him:

"For what cause is that boy Arthur made your King?"

"Sirs," said Merlin, "I will tell you the cause, because he is King Uther Pendragon's son. And whosoever saith 'Nay,' Arthur shall be King, and overcome all his enemies, and before he dies he shall long have been King of all England, and have under his sway Wales, Ireland, and Scotland, and more realms than I will now relate."

Some of the Kings marvelled at Merlin's words, and deemed it well that it should be as he said; and some of them, such as King Lot of Orkney, laughed at him; and others called him a wizard. But they all consented that King Arthur should come out and speak with them, and gave their assurance that he should come safely and should return safely.

So Merlin went to King Arthur, and told him what he had done, and bade him fear not, but come out boldly and speak with them.

"Spare them not," he said, "but answer them as their King and Chieftain, for ye shall overcome them all, whether they will or not."

Then King Arthur came out of his tower, having under his gown a cuirass of double mail; and there went with him the Archbishop of Canterbury, and Sir Baldwin, Sir Kay, and Sir Brastias. When he met the Kings there was no meekness, but stout words on both sides, King Arthur ready with an answer to all they said, and declaring that if he lived he would make them bow. They departed therefore in wrath, and King Arthur returned to the tower and armed himself and all his knights.

"What will you do?" said Merlin to the Kings; "you had better refrain, for you will not prevail here, were you ten times as many."

"Are we well advised to be afraid of a dream-reader?" sneered King Lot.

With that, Merlin vanished away, and came to King Arthur, and bade him set on them fiercely. And the magician counselled Arthur not to fight at first with the sword he had got by a miracle; but if he found himself getting the worst of the fight, then to draw it and do his best.

Meanwhile, three hundred of the best men who were with the Kings, went straight over to Arthur, and this comforted him greatly. All his knights fought gallantly, and the battle raged with fury. King Arthur himself was ever in the foremost of the press, till his horse was slain underneath him. And therewith King Lot smote down King Arthur.

Four of his knights rescued him and set him on horseback. Then he drew forth his sword, and it was so bright in his enemies' eyes that it gave light like thirty torches; and thus he drove back his foes and slew many of them.

Then the citizens of Carleon arose with clubs and stones, and slew many knights. But all the Kings banded together with their knights who were alive and so fled and departed.

And Merlin came to Arthur, and counselled him to follow them no farther.

THE BATTLE OF THE KINGS

AFTER the feast and the tourney Arthur came to London, and called all his Barons to a Council. For Merlin had told him that the six Kings who had made war upon him, and whom he had defeated, would hasten to wreak their vengeance on him and his lands. The Barons could give no counsel, but said they were big enough to fight.

"You say well," said Arthur, "I thank you for your good courage; but will all of you who love me speak with Merlin? You know well that he has done much for me, and knows many things, and when he is with you I wish that you would beseech him to give you his best advice."

All the Barons said they would gladly hear what Merlin counselled, so the magician was sent for.

"I warn you well," said Merlin, "that your enemies are passing strong for you, and they are as good men of arms as any alive. By this time, too, they have got to themselves four Kings more, and a mighty Duke, and unless our King can get more horsemen with him than are to be found within the bounds of his own realm, if he fight with them in battle he shall be overcome and slain."

"What is best to be done?" asked the Barons.

"I will tell you my advice," said Merlin. "There are two brethren beyond the sea, and they are both Kings, and marvellously powerful men. One is called King Ban, of Benwick, and the other King Bors, of Gaul—that is, France. And against these two brothers wars a mighty man, the King Claudas, and strives with them for a castle; and there is great war bewtixt them. But because Claudas is very rich he gets many good knights to fight for him, and for the most part puts these two Kings to the worse. Now this is my counsel—that our King and Sovereign Lord send to Kings Ban and Bors two trusty knights, with letters stating that if they will come and see Arthur and his Court, and help him in his wars, then he will swear to help them in their wars against King Claudas. Now, what do you say to this counsel?"

"This is well counselled!" said the King and the Barons.

So in all haste it was settled.

Ulfius and Brastias were chosen as the messengers, and they rode forth, well-horsed and well-armed; and so crossed the sea, and rode towards the city of Benwick. Here in a narrow place they were attacked by eight knights of King Claudas, who tried to kill them or take them prisoners. But Ulfius and Brastias, fighting with them two by two, in turn overcame them all, and left them lying sorely hurt and bruised on the field.

When they came to Benwick it fortunately happened that both the Kings, Ban and Bors, were there. As soon as the Kings knew they were messengers of Arthur's, they gave them the very heartiest greeting, and when Ban and Bors read the letters, they were made even more welcome than before.

So Ulfius and Brastias had good cheer, and rich gifts, as many as they could carry away, and they took back this answer with them—that the two Kings would come to Arthur in all the haste they could.

King Arthur was very glad to get this message, and, when the time came for the Kings to arrive, he proclaimed a great feast and went ten miles out of London to meet them. After the feast there was a splendid tournament, in which seven hundred knights took part. Arthur, Ban, and Bors, with the Archbishop of Canterbury, and Sir Ector (Kay's father) sat in a place covered with cloth of gold, like a hall, with ladies and gentlewomen, to behold who did best, and to give judgment thereon. The knights who won the prizes were three of King Arthur's household, Sir Kay, Sir Lucas, and Sir Griflet.

With the help of King Ban and King Bors Arthur utterly defeated and put to rout the eleven Kings who were warring against him. When his enemies were scattered, King Ban and Kings Bors, laden with rich gifts, returned to their own countries. And they made a compact with Arthur that if they had need of him to help them against King Claudas, they would send to him for succor; and on the other hand, if Arthur had need of them, he was to send, and they would not tarry.

A PROPHECY OF DOOM

After the departure of Ban and Bors King Arthur rode to Carleon. Then there arrived the wife of King Lot of Orkney, one of the Kings who had been fighting against him. She came in great state, in the manner of a messenger, but it was really to spy on the Court of King Arthur. With her were her four sons, Gawaine, Gaheris, Agravaine, and Gareth, and many other knights and ladies. Though very cunning and deceitful she was a most beautiful woman, therefore she quite won the heart of King Arthur. He did not know that in reality she was his own half-sister, for she was the daughter of his mother Igraine, who before her marriage with Uther Pendragon had been the wife of a mighty Duke of Cornwall. Another daughter was Morgan le Fay, who was extremely beautiful and treacherous, and well skilled in magic.

King Lot's wife stayed a month at Carleon, and then went away, and after her departure King Arthur dreamed a marvellous dream, which filled him with great dread. He thought that there came into this land griffins and serpents; and he thought that they burnt and slew all the people in the land, and then he thought he fought with them, and they did him passing great harm, and wounded him sorely, but at the last he slew them.

When the King awoke he was very sorrowful because of his dream, and so to put it out of his thoughts he made ready with many knights to ride hunting. As soon as he was in the forest the King saw a great hart before him, and he rode after it so fast that his poor horse fell exhausted.

While the King was sitting waiting for one of his men to fetch him another horse, Merlin came by in the likeness of a child of fourteen years, and saluting the King, asked why he was so pensive. Arthur replied that he had much to make him pensive, whereupon Merlin made him very angry by saying he knew all his thoughts, who he was, and all about him. Then Merlin departed, and presently came again in the likeness of an old man of four-score years of age, and in this guise he again asked the King why he was so sad.

"I may well be sad," said Arthur, "because of many things."

And he told the old man about his dream, and also about the strange child who had just been there, and who had told him things he never knew before about his own father and mother. Then Merlin told him that everything the child said was quite true; and he went on to say that in the years to come much evil would fall upon the land, for King Lot's wife would have a child who would destroy Arthur and all the knights of his realm.

"What are you," said Arthur, "that tell me these tidings?"

"I am Merlin," replied the magician, "and I was he in the child's likeness."

"Ah," said King Arthur, "you are a marvellous man; but I wonder much at your words that I must die in battle."

"Wonder not," said Merlin, "for it is God's will to punish your body for wrong deeds done on earth. But I may well be sorry," added the old man, "for I shall die a shameful

death—to be put into the earth alive; but you shall die an honorable death."

As they talked thus, there came one with the King's horse, so Arthur mounted, and Merlin got on another horse, and they rode to Carleon.

The prophecy that Merlin foretold of his own death really came to pass. For some years later the great magician fell in love with a damsel of the Court, named Vivien, who pretended to like him in return till she had learned all manner of things that she desired. He taught her all kinds of magic and enchantments, so that she could work spells herself. But Merlin got so foolish in his affection that he would never let her out of his sight, and the lady grew quite weary of his love, and longed to be free. She was afraid of Merlin because he was a magician, and she could find no way to get rid of him.

At last it happened that once Merlin showed her a wonderful rock, in which was a great stone that worked by enchantment. Then Vivien cunningly persuaded Merlin to step into the rock to let her know of the marvels there, but when he was once inside she replaced the great stone by the spells he had taught her, so that in spite of all his crafts he could never again come out. Then Vivien fled away and left Merlin in the rock.

Thus the prophecy relating to his own fate was fulfilled, and later on what he had foretold with regard to King Arthur also came to pass. For Merlin once said that the person who should destroy Arthur should be born on May Day. So the King sent for all the children who were born on the first of May; there were a great many sons of lords and ladies, and among the rest was his nephew Mordred, the son of King Lot's wife. All the children were put into a ship, and sent away out of the country, and some were only four weeks old. But the ship drove against a rock, and was wrecked to pieces, and all the children perished, excepting one. Little Mordred was cast up by the sea, and a good man found him, and took care of him till he was fourteen years old, when he brought him to Court. Mordred, like his mother, was very sly and treacherous, and as will be seen later on he brought much misery on the noble fellowship of the Knights of the Round Table.

Many of the lords and barons of the realm were very angry because of this loss of their children; but many put the blame more on Merlin than on Arthur; so what for dread and for love they held their peace.

THE KNIGHT OF THE FOUNTAIN

When King Arthur learned from Merlin that his mother Igraine was still alive, he sent for her in all haste; and the Queen came, and brought with her Morgan le Fay, her daughter, who was as fair a lady as any might be. Igraine had never known what became of the little babe she entrusted to Merlin, for she had never seen the child afterwards, and did not even know what name was given to it. Then Merlin took the King by the hand, saying, "This is your mother." Therewith Arthur took his mother, Queen Igraine, into his arms, and kissed her, and each wept over the other. Then the King commanded a feast to be held that lasted eight days.

One day there came to the Court a squire on horseback, leading a knight before him, wounded to death. He told how there was a knight in the forest who had reared a pavilion by a well, and how he had slain his master, a good knight; and he besought that his master might be buried, and some knight might revenge his death.

There was much stir in the Court because of this knight's death, every one giving his advice, and a young squire called Griflet, who was about the same age as Arthur, came to the King, and besought him to make him a knight.

"Thou art full young and tender," said Arthur, "to take so high an order on thee."

"Sir," said Griflet, "I beseech you to make me knight."

"Sir, it were great pity to lose Griflet," said Merlin, "for he will be a passing good man when he is of age abiding with you the terms of his life."

So the King made him knight.

"Now," he said, "since I have made you knight, you must give me a gift."

"What you will," said Griflet.

Then the King made him promise that when he had fought with the knight at the fountain he would return straight to the Court without further debate.

So Griflet took his horse in great haste, and got ready his shield, and took a spear in his hand, and rode at a gallop till he came to the fountain. There he saw a rich pavilion, and near by under a cloth stood a fair horse, well saddled and bridled, and on a tree a shield of many colors, and a great spear. Griflet smote on the shield with the butt of his spear, so that the shield fell to the ground.

With that the knight came out of the pavilion, and said: "Fair knight, why smote you down my shield?"

"Because I would joust with you," said Griflet.

"It is better you do not," said the knight, "for you are but young and lately made knight, and your might is nothing to mine."

"As for that," said Griflet, "I *will* joust with you."

"I am loath to do it," said the knight, "but since I needs must, I will make ready. Whence be ye?"

"Sir, I am of Arthur's Court."

The two knights ran together, so that Griflet's spear was all shivered to pieces, and therewith the other knight, whose name was Pellinore, smote Griflet through the shield and left side, and broke his own spear, while horse and knight

21

fell down.

When Pellinone saw Griflet lie so on the ground he alighted, and was very sad, for he thought he had slain him. He unlaced his helm, and gave him air, and set him again on his horse, saying he had a mighty heart, and if he lived he would prove a passing good knight. So Sir Griflet rode back to Court, where great dole was made for him. But through good doctors he was healed and saved.

King Arthur was very wrathful because of the hurt to Sir Griflet, and he commanded one of his men to have his horse and armor ready waiting for him outside the city before daylight on the following morning. On the morrow, before dawn, he mounted and took spear and shield, telling the man to wait there till he came again.

He rode softly till day, and then he was aware of Merlin being chased by three churls, who would have slain him. The King rode towards them, and bade them "Flee, churls!" They were frightened when they saw a knight, and fled.

"O, Merlin," said Arthur, "here hadst thou been slain, for all thy crafts, had I not been here!"

"Nay, not so," said Merlin, "for I could save myself if I would. And thou are nearer thy death than I am, for thou are going towards thy death, if God be not thy friend."

As they went thus talking they came to the fountain, and the rich pavilion there beside it. Then King Arthur was aware where sat a knight, armed, in a chair.

"Sir Knight," said Arthur, "for what cause abidest thou here, that no knight may ride this way unless he joust with thee? I counsel thee to leave that custom."

"This custom," said Pellinore, "I have used, and will use, despite who saith nay; and whoever is grieved with my custom, let him mend it who will."

"I will amend it," said Arthur.

"I shall prevent you," said Pellinore.

He quickly mounted his horse, adjusted his shield, and took his spear. They met so hard against each other's shields that their spears shivered. Thereupon Arthur at once pulled out his sword.

"Nay, not so," said the knight, "it is fairer that we twain run once more together with sharp spears."

"I would readily," said Arthur, "if I had any more spears."

"I have enough," said Pellinore.

A squire came and brought two good spears, and again the knight and the King spurred together with all their might, so that both the spears were broken off short. Then Arthur set hand on his sword.

"Nay," said the knight, "ye shall do better. Ye are a passing good jouster as ever I met withal, and for the love of the high order of knighthood let us joust once again."

"I assent," said Arthur.

Then two more great spears were brought, and each knight took one, and they ran together, so that Arthur's spear was all shivered. But Pellinore hit him so hard in the middle of the shield that horse and man fell to the earth. Then Arthur eagerly pulled out his sword, saying, "I will assay thee, Sir Knight, on foot, for I have lost the honor on horseback," and he ran towards him with his sword drawn.

When Pellinore saw that, he too alighted, for he thought it no honor to have a knight at such disadvantage, for himself to be on horseback, and the other on foot. Then began a strong battle with many great strokes, both hacking and hewing, till the field was wet with blood. They fought long, and rested, and then went to battle again. At last they both smote together, so that their swords met evenly, but Pellinore's sword smote Arthur's in two pieces, wherefore the King was much grieved.

Then said the knight unto Arthur:

"Thou are in danger whether I choose to save thee or to slay thee; and unless thou yield thee as overcome and recreant thou shalt die."

"As for death," said King Arthur, "welcome be it, when it cometh; but to yield me unto thee as recreant, I had rather die than be so ashamed." And with that he leaped unto Pellinore, and threw him down, and tore off his helm.

When the knight felt this he was sorely frightened, though he was a very big and mighty man; but he quickly got Arthur underneath, and raised off his helm, and would have smitten off his head.

But up came Merlin, who said:

"Knight, hold thy hand, for if thou slay that knight thou puttest this realm in the greatest damage that ever realm was in. For this knight is a man of more honor than thou are aware of."

"Why, who is he?" said Pellinore.

"It is King Arthur."

Then Pellinore would have slain himself, for dread of his wrath, and lifted up his sword. But Merlin cast an enchantment on the knight, so that he fell to the earth in a great sleep.

THE SWORD EXCALIBUR

AFTER throwing Pellinore into an enchanted sleep, Merlin took up King Arthur, and rode forth on Pellinore's horse.

"Alas!" said Arthur, "what hast thou done, Merlin? Hast thou slain this good knight by thy crafts? There lived not so worshipful a knight as he was; I would rather than a year's income that he were alive."

"Do not be troubled," said Merlin, "for he is less hurt than you. He is only asleep, and will awake within three hours. There liveth not a greater knight than he is, and he shall hereafter do you right good service. His name is Pellinore, and he shall have two sons, that shall be passing good men,—Percival of Wales, and Lamarack of Wales."

Leaving Sir Pellinore, King Arthur and Merlin went to a hermit, who was a good man, and skilled in the art of healing. He attended so carefully to the King's wounds, that in three days they were quite well, and Arthur was able to go on his way with Merlin. Then as they rode, Arthur said, "I have no sword."

"No matter," said Merlin, "near by is a sword that shall be yours if I can get it."

So they rode till they came to a lake, which was a fair water and broad; and in the midst of the lake, Arthur saw an arm, clothed in white samite, that held in its hand a beautiful sword.

"Lo," said Merlin, "yonder is the sword I spoke of."

With that they saw a damsel rowing across the lake.

"What damsel is that?" said Arthur.

"That is the Lady of the Lake," said Merlin, "and within that lake is a rock, and therein is as fair a place as any on earth, and richly adorned. This damsel will soon come to you; then speak you fair to her, so that she will give you that sword."

Presently the damsel came to Arthur, and saluted him, and he her again.

"Damsel," said Arthur, "what sword is that which yonder the arm holdeth above the water? I would it were mine, for I have no sword."

"Sir Arthur, King," said the damsel, "that sword is mine; the name of it is Excalibur, that is as much as to say *Cut-Steel*. If you will give me a gift when I ask you, ye shall have it."

"By my faith," said Arthur, "I will give you what gift ye shall ask."

"Well," said the damsel, "go you into yonder barge, and row yourself to the sword, and take it and the scabbard with you, and I will ask my gift when I see my time."

So King Arthur and Merlin alighted, and tied their horses to two trees, and went into the barge, and when they came to the sword that the hand held, Arthur lifted it by the handle, and took it with him. And the arm and hand went under the water; and so they came to the land, and rode away.

Then King Arthur looked on the sword, and liked it passing well.

"Which like you the better, the sword or the scabbard?" asked Merlin.

"I like the sword better," replied Arthur.

"You are the more unwise," said Merlin, "for the scabbard is worth ten of the sword. While you have the scabbard upon you, ye shall never lose any blood, be ye ever so sorely wounded. Therefore keep well the scabbard always with you."

So they returned to Carleon, where King Arthur's knights were passing glad to see him. When they heard of his adventures they marvelled that he would so jeopardy himself alone. But all men of honor said it was merry to be under such a chieftain who would put his person in adventures as other poor knights did.

Some time after this, Merlin again warned King Arthur to keep the scabbard of the sword Excalibur very securely, for as long as he had it upon him he would never lose any blood, however sorely he might be wounded. For greater safety, Arthur entrusted the sword and scabbard to his sister, Morgan le Fay. But Morgan le Fay was a false and treacherous woman. She loved another knight better than her husband King Uriens, or her brother King Arthur, and she made up a wicked plot, by which they would both be slain. Then she meant to marry this other knight, Sir Accolon, and place him on King Arthur's throne, when she herself would become Queen of the whole realm. Therefore she made by enchantment another scabbard exactly like Excalibur's, which she gave to Arthur when he was going to fight; but Excalibur and its scabbard she kept for Sir Accolon.

THE ROUND TABLE

When Arthur had been King for some years, and had fought and overcome many of his enemies, his Barons were anxious that he should take a wife, so according to his usual custom he went and consulted Merlin.

"It is well," said Merlin, "for a man of your bounty and nobleness should not be without a wife. Now is there any that you love more than another?"

"Yes," said King Arthur, "I love Guinevere, the daughter of King Leodegrance, of the land of Cameliard. Leodegrance holdeth in his house the Table Round, which he had of my father, Uther, and this damsel is the most noble and beautiful that I know living, or yet that ever I could find."

"Sir," said Merlin, "as to her beauty, she is one of the fairest alive. But if you loved her not as well as you do, I could find you a damsel of beauty and goodness, that would like you and please you—if your heart were not set. But where a man's heart is set, he will be loath to go back."

"That is truth," said King Arthur.

Then Merlin warned the King that it would not be wise for him to marry Guinevere; Merlin had the gift of prophecy, and knew that if this marriage took place much unhappiness would come of it. But nothing would persuade the King from his purpose. So Merlin carried a message to Leodegrance, who rejoiced greatly.

"Those are the best tiding I ever heard," he said, "that a King of prowess and nobleness will wed my daughter. And as for my lands I would give him them if I thought it would please him, but he hath lands enough, he needeth none, but I shall send him a gift which shall please him much more. For I shall give him the Round Table which Uther Pendragon gave me, and when it is full complete there are a hundred knights and fifty. As for a hundred good knights, I have them myself, but I lack fifty, for so many have been slain in my days."

So King Leodegrance delivered his daughter to Merlin, and the Round Table, with the hundred knights; and they rode briskly, with great royalty, by water and by land, till they came near to London.

When King Arthur heard of the coming of Guinevere, and the hundred knights with the Round Table, he made great joy because of their coming, and that rich present.

"This fair lady is passing welcome unto me," he said, "for I have loved her long, and therefore there is nothing so dear to me. And these knights with the Round Table please me more than right great riches."

Then in all haste the King commanded preparations for the marriage and coronation to be made in the most honorable way that could be devised; and he bade Merlin go forth and seek fifty knights of the greatest prowess and honor, and fill the vacant places at the Round Table.

Within a short time Merlin had found such knights as would fill twenty-eight places, but no more could he find.

Then the Archbishop of Canterbury was fetched, and he blessed the seats with great splendor and devotion, and there sat the eight-and-twenty knights in their seats.

When this was done, Merlin said:

"Fair sirs, ye must all arise and come to King Arthur to do him homage," so they arose and did their homage.

And when they were gone Merlin found in every seat letters of gold, that told the knights' names that had sat there; but two places were empty.

Soon after this came young Gawaine, son of King Lot of Orkney, and asked a gift of the King.

"Ask," said the King, "and I shall grant it you."

"Sir, I ask that ye will make me knight that same day ye shall wed Guinevere."

"I will do it with a good will," said King Arthur, "and do unto you all the honor I can, because you are my nephew, my sister's son."

So the King made Gawaine knight, and at the same time, at the wedding feast, he also knighted a son of King Pellinore, a noble and gallant youth, whose name was Tor.

Then King Arthur asked Merlin what was the cause why there were two places empty among the seats at the Round Table.

"Sir," said Merlin, "there shall no man sit in those places, except they shall be of the greatest honor. But in the Siege Perilous there shall no man sit therein but one, and if there be any so hardy to do it, he shall be destroyed; and he that shall sit there shall have no equal."

Therewith Merlin took King Pellinore by the hand, and leading him next the two seats and the Siege Perilous, he said in open audience:

"This is your place, and best worthy ye are to sit therein of any that is here."

At this Sir Gawaine sat in great envy, and he said to Gaheris, his brother:

"Yonder knight is put in great honor, which grieveth me

sorely, for he slew our father, King Lot; therefore I will slay him with a sword that was sent me, which is passing trenchant."

"Ye shall not do so at this time," said Gaheris, "for at present I am only a squire. When I am made knight I will be avenged on him; and therefore, brother, it is best ye endure till another time, that we may have him out of the Court; for if we killed him here we should trouble this high feast."

"I will do as you wish," said Gawaine.

Then was the high feast made ready, and the King was wedded at Camelot to Dame Guinevere, in the church of St. Stephen's, with great solemnity.

Then the King established all his knights, and to those who were not rich he gave lands, and charged them never to do outrage nor murders and always to flee treason. Also by no means to be cruel, but to give mercy to him that asked mercy, upon pain of forfeiture of their honor and lordship of King Arthur for evermore; and always to do ladies, damsels, and gentlewomen succor, upon pain of death. Also that no man should take battle in a wrongful quarrel for any law, nor for world's goods.

Unto this were all the Knights of the Round Table sworn, both old and young. And every year they renewed their vows at the high Feast of Pentecost.

THE MARVELLOUS ADVENTURE
OF THE MAGIC SHIP

It befell one day that Arthur and many of his knights rode hunting into a great forest; the King himself, Sir Accolon of Gaul, and King Uriens, husband of Morgan le Fay, followed a fine hart, and their horses were so swift that in a little while they were ten miles ahead of their companions. Worn out with the chase, at last their horses fell exhausted, but still in front of them they saw the hart, passing weary.

"What shall we do?" said King Arthur. "We are hard bestead."

"Let us go on foot," said King Uriens, "till we meet with some lodging."

Then they saw that the hart lay on the bank of a large lake, and the dogs had got hold of him, so King Arthur blew the "prise," which is the note blown by the hunter on the death of the quarry.

After this he looked all around, and saw before him on the lake a little ship, apparelled with silk, down to the water; and the ship came right up to them and grounded on the sands. King Arthur went to the bank and looked in, and saw no earthly creature therein.

"Come," said the King, "let us see what is in the ship."

So they all three went in, and found it richly hung with cloth of silk. By then it was dark night, and suddenly there were about them a hundred torches, set upon all sides of the ship, which gave great light. Therewith came out twelve fair damsels, who saluted King Arthur on their knees, and called him by his name, and said he was right welcome, and such cheer as they had he should have of the best. The King thanked them courteously.

The damsels led the King and his two companions into a beautiful chamber, where there was a table richly spread with all manner of good things; and here they were served with all the wines and meats they could think of, which made the King greatly marvel, for he had never fared better in his life at any one supper.

When they had supped at their leisure King Arthur was led into another chamber, more richly adorned than he had ever seen; and so also was King Uriens served; and Sir Accolon was led into a third chamber, passing richly and well adorned; and so they went gladly to bed, and fell asleep at once.

But on the morrow when he awoke, King Uriens found himself in Camelot, with his wife, Morgan le Fay, and this greatly astonished him, for on the evening before, he was two days' journey from Camelot.

And when King Arthur awoke he found himself in a dark prison, hearing about him many complaints of woeful knights.

"What are ye that so complain?" said King Arthur.

"We be here twenty knights prisoners," said they, "and some of us have lain here seven years, and some more and some less."

"For what cause?" said Arthur.

"We will tell you," said the knights.

"The lord of this castle is named Sir Damas, and he is

the falsest knight alive, and full of treason, and the veriest coward that ever lived. He has a younger brother, a good knight of prowess, named Sir Ontzlake, and this traitor, Damas, the elder brother, will give him no part of his heritage, except what Sir Ontzlake can keep through his own prowess. But the younger brother holds a full fair manor and a rich, and therein he dwells in honor, and is well beloved of all people, while Sir Damas is equally ill beloved, for he is without mercy, and a coward. Great war has been betwixt them both, but Sir Ontzlake always gets the better; and he keeps offering Damas to fight for the heritage, man against man, and if he will not do it himself, to find a knight to fight for him.

"Unto this Sir Damas agreed, but he is so hated that there is never a knight will fight for him. Seeing this, Damas hath daily lain in wait with many knights, and taken all the other knights in this country separately by force, as they rode on their adventures, and brought them to his prison. And many good knights, to the number of eighteen, have died in this prison from hunger. If any of us that have been here would have fought with his brother Ontzlake, he would have delivered us, but because this Damas is so false and so full of treason we would never fight for him. And we be so lean with hunger we can hardly stand on our feet."

"God in His mercy deliver you," said Arthur.

Just then there came a damsel to Arthur, and asked him, "What cheer?"

"I cannot say," said he.

"Sir," said she, "if you will fight for my lord you shall be delivered out of prison, otherwise you will never escape with life."

"Now," said Arthur, "that is hard, but I would rather

fight with a knight than die in prison. On condition that I may be delivered, and all these prisoners, I will do the battle."

"Yes," said the damsel.

"I am ready," said Arthur, "if I had horse and armor."

"Ye shall lack nothing," was the reply.

"It seems to me, damsel, that I have seen you in the Court of Arthur?"

"Nay," said the damsel, "I never went there, I am the daughter of the lord of this Castle."

Yet she was false, for she was one of the damsels of Morgan le Fay.

Then she went quickly to Sir Damas, and told him how Arthur would do battle for him, and so he sent for Arthur. And when he came he was so handsome and well-made that all the knights who saw him said it was a pity that such a knight should die in prison.

Then Sir Damas and he agreed that he should fight for him on this covenant—that all the other knights should be delivered. Sir Damas swore to Arthur that this should be done, and Arthur, in return, swore to do battle to the uttermost.

And with that, all the twenty knights were brought out of the dark prison into the hall, and set at liberty. And so they all waited to see the battle.

THE FALSE CRAFT OF MORGAN LE FAY

Now let us turn to Sir Accolon of Gaul, who was with King Arthur and King Uriens when they went to sleep on the magic ship.

When he awoke he found himself by the side of a deep well, within half a foot of the edge, in great peril of death. Out of the fountain came a pipe of silver, and out of the pipe ran water all on high in a marble basin.

When Sir Accolon saw this, he said:

"Heaven save my lord King Arthur and King Uriens, for these damsels in the ship have betrayed us. They were demons and no women, and if I escape this misadventure, I shall destroy wherever I find them all false damsels that use enchantments."

At the moment up came a dwarf with a great mouth and a flat nose, who saluted Sir Accolon, and said he had come from Queen Morgan le Fay.

"She greeteth you well, and biddeth you be of strong heart, for ye shall figfht tomorrow with a knight at the hour of noon, and therefore she hath sent you here Excalibur, Arthur's sword, and the scabbard. She biddeth you, as ye love her, that ye do battle to the uttermost, without any mercy, exactly as you promised her when ye spake together in private. And the damsel who brings her the head of the knight with whom ye shall fight, she will make her a queen."

"Now I understand you well," said Accolon. "I shall keep my promise now that I have the sword. Command me unto my lady queen, and tell her all shall be done that I promised her, or else I shall die for it. Now I suppose," he added, "she has made all these crafts and enchantments for this battle?"

"Ye may well believe it," said the dwarf.

Then up came a knight with a lady and six squires, who saluted Sir Accolon, and begged him to go and rest himself at his manor. This knight was Sir Ontzlake, brother of Sir Damas, with whom King Arthur had already promised Damas to fight. So Accolon mounted a spare horse, and went with the knight to a fair manor by a priory, where he had passing good cheer.

Sir Damas, meanwhile, had sent to his brother to bid him make ready by the next day, at the hour of noon, and to be in the field to fight with a good knight, for he had found a good knight who was ready to do battle at all points. When this word came to Sir Ontzlake he was much disturbed, for he was already wounded through both thighs with a spear, but hurt as he was he would have taken the battle in hand. But when Sir Accolon heard of the battle, and how Ontzlake was wounded, he said he would fight for him, because Morgan le Fay had sent him Excalibur and the sheath, to fight with a knight on the morrow. Then Sir Ontzlake was very glad, and thanked Sir Accolon with all his heart that he would do so much for him.

The next morning when King Arthur was mounted and ready to ride forth, there came a damsel from Morgan le Fay, who brought to the King a sword like Excalibur, and the scabbard, and said:

"Morgan le Fay sendeth you here your sword for great love."

He thanked her, and thought it had been so, but she was false, for the sword and the scabbard were counterfeit, and brittle, and false.

Then King Arthur and Sir Accolon made ready, and their horses rushed so swiftly together, that each smote the other with their spear's head in the midst of the shield, so that both horse and man were borne to the earth; and then both knights started up and pulled out their swords. The wicked Queen had cast a spell over them, so that neither knew the other. But while they were thus fighting, came the damsel of the lake, who had put Merlin under the stone, and she came for love of Arthur, for she knew how Morgan le Fay had so ordained that Arthur should be slain that day; therefore Vivien came to save his life.

Thus they went eagerly to the battle, and gave many great strokes. But King Arthur's sword never hit like Sir Accolon's sword; nearly every stroke that Accolon gave he sorely wounded Arthur, so that it was a marvel he stood, and always his blood fell from him fast. When Arthur saw the ground all covered with blood, he was dismayed, and guessed there was treason, and that his sword had been changed. For his sword bit not steel as it was wont to do, wherefore he feared to be killed; it seemed to him that the sword in Accolon's hand was Excalibur, for at every stroke it drew blood, but he was so full of knighthood that he nobly endured the pain. And all the men that beheld him said they never saw knight fight so well as Arthur did, considering how sorely he was wounded. All the people were sorry for him, but the two brothers Sir Damas and Sir Ontzlake would not agree, so the knights went on fighting fiercely. Then suddenly King Arthur's sword broke at the hilt, and fell in the grass, leaving the pommel and the handle in his hand. When he saw that, he greatly feared he would be killed, but always he held up his shield, and lost no ground, and bated no cheer.

HOW KING ARTHUR
GOT HIS OWN SWORD AGAIN

When Sir Accolon saw that King Arthur's sword was broken he tried to tempt him to give in.

"Knight, thou art overcome and mayst not endure, and also thou are weaponless, and thou hast lost much blood; I am full loath to slay thee; therefore yield thee to me as recreant."

"Nay," said Arthur, "I may not so, for I have promised to do battle to the uttermost by the faith of my body while life lasteth; and therefore I had rather die with honor than live with shame; and if it were possible to die a hundred times, I would rather die so often than yield me to thee, for though I lack weapon, I shall lack no honor, and if thou slay me weaponless, that shall be thy shame."

"Well," said Accolon, "as for the shame I will not spare; now keep thee from me, for thou are but a dead man," and therewith he gave him such a stroke that he fell nearly to the earth, and he hoped Arthur would have cried him mercy.

But the King pressed forward to Accolon, and gave him such a buffet with the pommel of the broken sword that the knight went three strides back.

When the damsel of the lake beheld Arthur, and how valorous he was, and the false treason that was wrought to have him slain, she had great pity that so good a knight and noble a man should be destroyed. And by her enchantment, at the next stroke the sword fell out of Accolon's hand to the earth. Then Arthur leaped lightly to it, and got it in his hand, and immediately he knew that it was his own sword Excalibur.

"Thou hast been from me all too long," he cried, "and much damage hast thou done me."

Then he espied the scabbard hanging by Accolon's side, and he suddenly started to him, and seized the scabbard, and threw it from him as far as he could.

"O knight!" he said, "now are ye come unto your death, for I warrant ye shall be as well rewarded with this sword before ever we depart, as thou hast rewarded me." Therewith he rushed on him with all his might, and pulled him to the ground, and dashed off his helm, and gave such a buffet on the head that it nearly killed him.

"Now I will slay thee," said Arthur.

"Slay me ye well may, if it please you," said Accolon, "for ye are the best knight that ever I found, and I see well that God is with you. But because I promised to do this battle to the uttermost, and never to be recreant while I lived, therefore shall I never yield me with my mouth, but God do with my body what He will."

Then King Arthur remembered him, and thought he must have seen this knight.

"Now tell me," he said, "or I will slay thee, of what country art thou, and of what Court?"

"Sir Knight," said Sir Accolon, "I am of the Court of King Arthur, and my name is Accolon of Gaul."

Then was Arthur more dismayed than before, for he remembered his sister Morgan le Fay, and the enchantment of the ship.

"O, Sir Knight," he said, "I pray you tell me who gave you this sword?"

Then Sir Accolon told him how Morgan le Fay had sent it him to the intent that he might kill King Arthur her brother. For King Arthur was the man in the world whom she most hated, because of his valor and renown. And if she should succeed in killing Arthur by her crafts, she would also lightly slay her husband, and then she had devised that Accolon should be king in the land, and she would be queen.

"But that is now done," said Accolon, "for I am sure of my death. But now I have told you truth, I pray you tell me whence ye are, and of what Court?"

"O, Accolon," said Arthur, "now I let you know that I am King Arthur, to whom thou hast done great damage."

When Accolon heard that, he cried aloud:

"Fair sweet lord, have mercy on me, for I knew you not!"

"Mercy thou shalt have, Sir Accolon," said Arthur, "because I see that just now thou knewest not my person. But I understand well by thy words that thou hast agreed to my death, and therefore thou art a traitor; but I blame thee the less, for my sister Morgan le Fay by her false crafts made thee agree and consent to her wickedness."

Then King Arthur called the keepers of the field, and told them what had happened.

"Had either of us known the other, here had been no battle, nor stroke stricken," he said.

Then Sir Accolon cried aloud to all the knights and men that were gathered together, "O lords, this noble knight that I have fought with, for which I sorely repent, is the greatest man of prowess, of manhood, and of worship in the world, for it is King Arthur himself, the liege lord of us all!"

Then all the people fell down on their knees, and cried

mercy of King Arthur, which the King at once granted.

Then he went on to deliver judgment between the two brothers for whom he and Sir Accolon had fought. As Sir Damas was a haughty knight, and full of villainy, he commanded that he should give to his younger brother the manor and all that belonged to it, and that in return Sir Ontzlake should yearly give him a palfrey to ride upon, for that would become him better to ride on than a charger. And on pain of death Sir Damas was evermore forbidden to distress any knights-errant who rode on adventure. And to those twenty knights whom he had so long kept prisoners he was to restore all their armor.

"And if any of them come to my Court and complain of thee, by my head thou shalt die for it," said the King. "And to you, Sir Ontzlake, because ye are named a good knight, and full of prowess, and true and gentle in all your deeds, this shall be your charge: I bid you that in all goodly haste ye come unto me and my Court; and ye shall be a knight of mine; and if your deeds be truly thus, I will so prefer you by the grace of God, that ye shall in a short time easily live in as much state as Sir Damas."

Then King Arthur and Sir Accolon rode to a rich abbey near at hand, to rest themselves and have their wounds attended to, and soon the King was well recovered. But Sir Accolon died within four days, for he was sorely hurt.

When Accolon was dead, the King had him sent on on a horse-bier, with six knights of Camelot, and said:

"Bear him to my sister Morgan le Fay, and say that I send him to her as a present; and tell her that I have my sword Excalibur and the scabbard."

THE MANTLE OF PRECIOUS STONES

When tidings came to Morgan le Fay that Accolon was dead, and that Arthur had his sword again, she was so sorrowful that her heart was like to break. But because she would not have it known, she outwardly kept her countenance and made no sign of sorrow. But she knew well that if she abode where she was till her brother Arthur came, no gold would save her life, for he had sworn to be avenged.

She went, therefore, to Queen Guinevere, and asked her leave to ride into the country.

"You can wait," said Queen Guinevere, "till your brother the King comes."

"I can not," said Morgan le Fay, "for I have such hasty tidings that I may not tarry."

"Well," said Guinevere, "you may depart when you will."

So early on the morrow, before it was day, she took her horse, and rode all that day and most part of the night, and on the morrow by noon she came to the same abbey where King Arthur was. Knowing he was there, she asked how he was, and they answered that he was asleep in bed, for he had had but little rest these three nights.

"Well," she said, "I charge you that none of you awake him till I do."

Then she alighted off her horse, and thought to steal away

Excalibur, his sword. So she went straight to his chamber, and no man durst disobey her command, and there she found Arthur asleep on his bed, and Excalibur in his right hand naked. When she saw that, she was greatly vexed that she could not get the sword unless she waked him, which she knew well would be her death. So she took the scabbard, and went her way on horseback.

When the King awoke and missed the scabbard he was very angry, and he asked who had been there. They told him it was his sister, Morgan le Fay, who had put the scabbard under her mantle, and was gone.

"Alas!" said Arthur, "falsely have ye watched me!"

"Sir," said they all, "we durst not disobey your sister's command."

"Fetch the best horse that can be found," said the King, "and bid Sir Ontzlake arm in all haste, and take another good horse and ride with me."

So the King and Ontzlake were quickly well armed, and rode after Queen Morgan le Fay. Presently they met a cowherd, whom they asked if any lady had lately ridden that way.

"Sir," said the poor man, "just now came a lady riding with forty horsemen, and she rode to yonder forest."

Then they spurred their horses, and followed fast, and within a little while Arthur had a sight of Morgan le Fay; then he chased as fast as he could. When she espied him following her, she quickened her pace through the forest till she came to a plain. And when she saw she could not escape she rode to a lake thereby, and said: "Whatsoever becometh of me, my brother shall not have this scabbard," and she threw it into the deepest of the water, so that it sank, for it was heavy with gold and precious stones.

Then she rode into a valley, where many great stones were, and seeing that she must be overtaken she shaped herself, by enchantment, into a great marble stone. When the King came, with Ontzlake, he did not know his sister and her men, nor one knight from another.

"Ah," said the King, "here ye may see the vengeance of God, and now I am sorry that this misadventure is befallen."

Then he looked for the scabbard, but it could not be found. So he returned to the abbey where he came from.

When Arthur had gone, Morgan le Fay turned herself and all her knights back into the likeness that they were before, and said: "Sirs, now we may go where we will."

So they departed into the country of Gore, where she was richly received; and she made her castles and towns passing strong, for always she dreaded much King Arthur.

After the King had well rested at the abbey, he rode to Camelot, where he found his Queen and his Barons right glad at his coming. When they heard of his strange adventures they all marvelled at the falsehood of Morgan le Fay; and because of her wicked enchantments many of the knights wished her burned.

The next day there came a damsel from Morgan to King Arthur, and she brought with her the richest mantle that ever was seen in that Court, for it was set as full of precious stones as they could stand one by another, and they were the richest stones that ever the King saw.

"Your sister sendeth you this mantle," said the damsel, "and desireth that you should take this gift of her, and in what thing she hath offended you she will mend it at your own pleasure."

When the King beheld the mantle it pleased him much, but he said but little.

With that came the damsel of the lake to the King, and said: "Sir, I must speak with you in private."

"Say on," said the King, "what ye will."

"Sir," said the damsel, "do not put this mantle on you till ye have seen more, and in no wise let it come on you nor on any knight of yours till ye command the bringer thereof to put it on her."

"Well," said King Arthur, "it shall be done as you counsel me." Then he said to the damsel who came from his sister, "Damsel, this mantle that ye have brought me I will see it upon you."

"Sir," said she, "it will not beseem me to wear a King's garment."

"By my head," said Arthur, "ye shall wear it before it goes on my back, or any man's that is here."

So the mantle was put on her, and immediately she fell dead, and never spoke a word after, for she was burned to a cinder.

Then was Arthur terribly wroth, more than he was beforehand, and he said to King Uriens:

"My sister, your wife, is always about to betray me, and well I know that either you or my nephew, your son, is in council with her to have me destroyed. As for you, I do not much think you are in her council, for Accolon confessed to me with his own mouth that she would have destroyed you as well as me, therefore I hold you excused. But as for your son, Sir Uwaine, I hold him suspected, therefore I charge you to put him out of my Court."

So Sir Uwaine was dismissed.

When Sir Gawaine, King Lot's son, knew this, he made ready to go with him.

"Whoso banisheth my cousin shall banish me," he said, so

they two departed.

When Arthur was aware that Sir Gawaine had left the Court, there was much sorrow among all the lords.

"Now," said Gaheris, Gawaine's brother, "we have lost two good knights for the sake of one."

THE DREAM OF THE DRAGON
AND THE BOAR

AFTER long war King Arthur rested, and held a royal feast with his allies of king, princes, and noble knights, all of the Round Table. And as he sat on his royal throne, there came into the hall twelve ancient men, bearing each of them a branch of olive, in token that they came as ambassadors and messengers from Lucius, Emperor of Rome. Having done their obeisance to the King they delivered their greeting from the Emperor Lucius, commanding Arthur to acknowledge him as lord, and pay the tribute due from England to Rome, as his father and predecessors had done before. If he refused this demand, then strong war would be made against him, his realms and his subjects, so that it would be a perpetual example to all kings and princes who dared to deny tribute to Rome, sovereign of the whole world.

When they had delivered their message, the King commanded them to withdraw, and called together all his lords and knights of the Round Table, for counsel on the matter, and to give their advice. They all said the demand for tribute was unjust, and every man agreed to make war and to aid after his power; the King of Scotland, the King of Little Britain, and the lord of West Wales, all promised men and money, and Sir Lancelot and the other knights also promised likewise. When King Arthur understood their courage and goodwill he thanked them heartily. The ambassadors, laden with presents, were sent back to Rome with

the answer that he owed no tribute to earthly prince, Christian or heathen; he claimed sovereignty of the realm of England by right of his predecessors; and he was fully determined to go with a strong and powerful army to Rome, by the Grace of God to take possession of the empire, and to subdue those that were rebellious.

When the ambassadors returned with this message to Lucius, the Emperor sent over the whole world, to all dominions that were subject to the Empire of Rome, to summon warriors to fight against Arthur. So a great multitude of kings and dukes and captains, and thousands of people assembled round about Rome. Also he had with him fifty giants, who were ordained to guard his person, and to break the front of the battle of King Arthur.

In the meanwhile King Arthur held a Parliament at York, and appointed that, during his absence, Queen Guinevere and the realm should be in the governance of Sir Baldwin of Britain and Sir Constantine, son of Sir Cador of Cornwall, who after his death, became king of the realm. Then King Arthur, with all his army, departed, sailing from Sandwich, with a great multitude of ships, galleys, boats, and men-of-war.

And as the King lay in his cabin in the ship he fell asleep, and dreamed a marvellous dream. It seemed to him that a dreadful dragon drowned much of his people, and he came flying out of the west; his head was enamelled with azure, and his shoulders shone as gold, his body like mail of a marvellous hue, his tail full of tatters, his feet covered with sable, and his claws like fine gold; a hideous flame of fire flew out of his mouth, as if land and water all flamed fire.

After him there came out of the east a grimly boar, all black, in a cloud; his paws were as big as a post, he was rough and rugged looking—the vilest beast that ever man saw; he roared and growled so hideously that it was a marvel to hear.

Then the dreadful dragon advanced, and fought with the boar, who gnashed at him with his tusks, so that all the sea was red with blood; but at last the dragon smote the boar to powder, both flesh and bones, so that it was scattered in fragments all abroad on the sea.

Therewith King Arthur awoke, and was sorely abashed because of this dream, and he sent at once to a wise philosopher, commanding him to tell the meaning of it.

"Sir," said the philosopher, "the dragon that thou dreamedst of betokeneth thine own person, and the color of his wings be the realms that thou hast won; and his tail which is all tattered signifieth the noble Knights of the Round Table. And the boar which the dragon slew, coming from the clouds, betokeneth some tyrant that tormenteth the people, or else thou art like to fight with some giant thyself, whose peer ye never yet saw. Wherefore of this dreadful dream doubt ye nothing, but as a conqueror go forth thyself."

Soon after King Arthur's dream of the dragon and the boar they arrived in France, and here a husbandman came to Arthur and told him that for seven years a fearful giant had been ravaging the land of Brittany, and had slain, murdered, and devoured many people of the country. Lately he had seized the Duchess of Brittany as she rode with her train, and had carried her to his dwelling, which was in a mountain, to keep to her life's end. Many people followed her, more than five hundred, but not all of them together could rescue her.

"She was wife to thy cousin, Duke Howell, whom we call

full nigh of thy blood," ended the man; "now, as thou art a rightful King, have pity on this lady; and, as thou art a noble conqueror, revenge us all."

"Alas!" said King Arthur, "this is a great mischief! I had rather than the best realm I have that I had been a furlong before him, to have rescued that lady. Now, fellow, canst thou bring me there where this giant haunteth?"

"Yes, sir," said the good man, "lo, yonder where thou seeest those two great fires, there thou shalt find him, and more treasure than I suppose there is in all France."

When the King understood this piteous case, he returned into his tent. There he called to him Sir Kay and Sir Bedivere, and commanded them secretly to make ready horse and armor for himself and them twain, for after evensong he would ride on pilgrimage with those two only to St. Michael's Mount. So they three departed, and rode forth as fast as ever they could, till they came to the foot of the Mount. There they alighted, and the King commanded them to tarry there, for he would himself go up into the Mount.

He ascended the hill till he came to a great fire, and there he found a widow wringing her hands, and making great sorrow, sitting by a grave new-made. King Arthur saluted her, and asked her why she made such lamentation.

"Sir knight, speak soft," she answered, "for yonder is a devil. If he hear thee speak he will come and destroy thee. O unhappy man, what does thou here in this mountain? If ye were fifty such as ye be, ye would not be able to make resistance against this monster. Here lieth a duchess dead, who was the fairest of all the world, wife to Howell, Duke of Brittany—he hath murdered her."

"Dame," said the King, "I come from the noble conqueror King Arthur, to treat with that tyrant for his liege people."

"Fie upon such treaties!" said the widow, "for he setteth not by the King, nor by any man. Beware, approach him not too near, for he hath vanquished fifteen kings, and hath made him a coat of precious stones, embroidered with their beards, which they sent him to save their people this last Christmas. And if thou wilt, speak with him at yonder great fire, at supper."

"Well," said Arthur, "for all your fearful words, I will accomplish my message."

Then he went forth by the crest of the hill, and saw the giant where he sat at supper, gnawing a huge bone, and baking his broad limbs by the fire, while three fair damsels turned three spits, whereon were broached twelve young children, like young birds. When King Arthur beheld this piteous sight, he had great compassion for them, so that his heart bled for sorrow, and he hailed the giant, saying:

"He that wieldeth all the world give thee short life and shameful death! Why hast thou murdered these young innocent children, and slain this duchess? Arise and make ready, thou glutton, for this day thou shalt die at my hand."

Then the giant started up at once, and took a great club in his hand, and smote at the King, so that his helmet was crushed, and the King hit him again, and wounded him sorely. Then the giant threw away his club, and caught the King in his arms, so that he crushed his ribs. Then the three maidens knelt down and called to Christ for help and comfort to Arthur. The King wrestled and strove, so that sometimes he was under, and sometimes above, and thus wrestling and striving, they rolled down the hill, till they came to the sea-mark; and ever as they wrestled, Arthur smote the giant with his dagger; and thus it happened they came to the place where the two knights were with Arthur's horse.

When they saw the King in the giant's arms they came and set him free, and by that time the giant was dead. King Arthur commanded them to smite off his head, and to set it on a spear, and bear it to Duke Howell, and tell him that his enemy was slain; and afterwards to put the head on a tower that all people might behold it.

"And go ye two up the mountain, and fetch me my shield, my sword, and the club of iron," said King Arthur. "And as for the treasure, take ye it, for ye shall find there goods out of number. So that I have the kirtle and the club, I desire no more."

Then the knights fetched the club and the kirtle, and some of the treasure they took to themselves, and returned again to the army. And this was immediately known all through the country, wherefore the people came and thanked the King. But he answered:

"Give the thanks to God, and part the goods among you."

And after that, King Arthur commanded his cousin Duke Howell that he should ordain a church to be built on that same mountain, in honor of St. Michael.

The next day the King set out again on his expedition against the Emperor Lucius. After many fierce battles he defeated the Romans, killed Lucius, and was crowned Emperor of all the lands from Rome to France. Then he returned home in triumph with all his knights, crossing the sea, and landing at Sandwich, where Queen Guinevere, his wife, came to meet him. All the people in every city and burgh received him nobly, and great gifts were presented to welcome him at his home-coming.

SIR LANCELOT OF THE LAKE

THE STRONG KNIGHT OF THE FOREST

At the Court of King Arthur were many valiant knights, and some among them increased so in arms and worship that they surpassed all their fellows in prowess and noble deeds. But chief among them all was Sir Lancelot of the Lake, for in all tournaments and jousts and deeds of arms, both for life and death, he excelled all other knights, and never at any time was he overcome, unless it were by treason or enchantment.

Because of this Queen Guinevere held him in higher favor than all other knights, and Sir Lancelot for his part loved the Queen above all other ladies and damsels all his life; and for her he did many deeds of arms, and more than once saved her from death by his noble chivalry.

When King Arthur returned to England from Rome all the Knights of the Round Table resorted to him, and many jousts and tournaments were held. Sir Lancelot rested himself for some time with sport and play, but at last he longed again to make trial of himself in strange adventures. Therefore, bidding his nephew Sir Lionel make ready, they mounted their horses, armed at all points, and rode into a deep forest, and so on to a wide plain.

About noon the weather was very hot, and Sir Lancelot felt sleepy. Then Sir Lionel espied a great apple-tree that stood by a hedge, and he said:

"Brother, yonder is a fair shadow; there we may rest ourselves and our horses."

"It is well said," answered Sir Lancelot; "for this seven years I have not been so sleepy as I am now."

So they alighted there, and tied their horses to a tree, and Lancelot lay down, and put his helm under his head, and fell very fast asleep. But Lionel kept awake.

In the meanwhile came three knights riding, fleeing as fast as ever they could ride, and these three were followed by one knight. When Sir Lionel saw him he thought he had never seen so great a knight, nor so well faring a man, nor one so well apparelled. In a little while this strong knight overtook one of the three, and smote him to the cold earth, so that he lay still. Then he rode to the second knight, and smote him so that both man and horse fell down. Then he rode straight at the third knight and smote him a spear's length behind his horse's tail. Then he alighted, and bound all the three knights fast with the reins of their own bridles.

When Sir Lionel saw him do thus he thought he would assay him, so making ready he took his horse very quietly in order not to wake Sir Lancelot. He soon overtook the strong knight, and bade him turn, but the latter smote Sir Lionel so hard that he bore horse and man to the earth. Then he alighted and bound him fast, and threw him and the three other knights each across his own horse, and rode with them away to his Castle. When he got there he took away their armor, and beat them with thorns, and put them into a deep dungeon, where there were many more knights who made much lamentation.

Sir Ector de Maris in the meanwhile, finding that Sir Lancelot had left the Court to seek adventures, was angry with himself, and made ready to go in search of him. Riding through a great forest he met a man who looked like a forester, and he asked this man if he knew of any adventures near at hand. The forester replied that within a mile was a strong manor, with a moat all round it; and near the manor on the left hand was a ford for horses to drink from. At the ford grew a beautiful tree on which hung many fair shields that had once belonged to gallant knights. On the tree hung also a basin of brass and copper, and the forester bade Sir Ector strike thrice on the basin with the butt of his spear, and he would soon hear new tidings, unless he had the greatest luck of any knight who had passed through that forest for many a year.

Thanking the man Sir Ector departed, and soon came to the tree, where he found many fair shields; among them he saw his brother's shield, Sir Lionel, and many more that he knew were his fellows of the Round Table, which grieved his heart, and he promised to revenge his brother.

He beat at once on the basin, as if he were mad, and then he gave his horse drink at the ford. There came a knight behind him, and bade him come out of the water and make him ready. Sir Ector turned sharply, and cast his spear, and smote the other knight a great buffet, so that his horse reeled twice round.

"That was well done," said the strong knight, "and knightly hast thou stricken me;" and therewith he rushed his horse on Sir Ector, and catching him under his right arm, he bore him clean out of the saddle, and rode with him away into his own hall, where he threw him down in the middle of the floor.

The name of this knight was Sir Turquine.

"Because thou hast done this day more unto me than any knight did these twelve years," said he to Sir Ector, "now will I grant thee thy life, if thou wilt swear to be my prisoner all the days of thy life."

"Nay," said Sir Ector, "that I will never promise thee."

"I am sorry for that," said Sir Turquine.

Then he took Sir Ector's armor away, and beat him with thorns, and put him down in a deep dungeon, where he found many companions whom he knew. But when he saw Sir Lionel there he made great sorrow. "Alas," he said, "where is my brother Sir Lancelot?"

"I left him asleep under an apple-tree, when I went from him," said Lionel, "and what is become of him I cannot tell you."

"Alas," said the knights, "unless Sir Lancelot help us we shall never be delivered, for we know now no knight that is able to match our master Turquine."

THE FOUR QUEENS

IN the meanwhile Sir Lancelot of the Lake still lay asleep under the apple-tree. Then about noon there came by four Queens of great estate; and in order that the heat of the sun should not annoy them there rode four knights beside them, bearing a cloth of green silk on four spears betwixt them and the sun; and the Queens rode on four white mules.

Thus as they rode they heard near them a great horse grimly neigh, and they were aware of a sleeping knight that lay all armed under an apple-tree; and directly these Queens looked on his face they knew it was Sir Lancelot. Then they began to quarrel as to which should win his love, for each one of them said he should be her champion knight.

"Do not let us quarrel," said Morgan le Fay, King Arthur's sister, "I will put an enchantment on him that he shall not wake in six hours, and I will carry him away into my Castle. And when he is safely within my hold, I will take the enchantment from him, and then let him choose which of us he shall have."

So they threw a spell over Sir Lancelot, and then they laid him on his shield and bore him so on horseback between two knights to the Castle Chariot. There he was placed in a cold chamber, and at night they sent to him a fair damsel with his supper. By that time the enchantment was past, and when she came she saluted him, and asked, "What cheer?"

"I cannot say, fair damsel" said Sir Lancelot, "for I know not how I came into this Castle, unless it were by enchantment."

"Sir," said she, "ye must make good cheer, and if ye be such a knight as ye are said to be, I will tell you more tomorrow at dawn of day."

So she departed, and there Lancelot lay all night without comfort of anybody.

On the morrow early came these four Queens, richly bedecked, and they bade him good-morrow, and he them again. Then they told him they knew well who he was—Sir Lancelot of the Lake, King Ban's son, the noblest knight alive.

"We know well that no lady has thy love, but one, and that is Queen Guinevere; now thou shalt lose her for ever, and she thee, therefore thou must now choose one of us four. I am the Queen Morgan le Fay, Queen of the land of Gore; and here is the Queen of North Wales; and the Queen of Eastland; and the Queen of the Outer Isles. Now choose ye one of us which thou wilt have, or else die in this prison."

"That is a hard case," said Sir Lancelot, "that either I must die or choose one of you. Yet I would rather die in this prison with honor than have one of you to be my lady against my will. And therefore ye are answered; I will have none of you, for ye are false enchantresses."

"Well," said the Queens, "is this your answer, that ye will refuse us?"

"Yea, on my life," said Sir Lancelot, "ye are refused by me."

So they departed, and left him there alone in great sorrow.

At noon came the damsel to him with his dinner, and asked him "What cheer?"

"Truly, fair damsel," said Lancelot, "in all the days of my life never so ill."

"Sir," said she, "I am sorry for that, but if you will be ruled by me I will help you out of this distress, and ye shall have no shame or villainy, if you will make me a promise."

"That I will grant you; and I am sore afraid of these Queen sorceresses, for they have destroyed many a good knight."

Then the damsel went on to say that on the next Tuesday her father had made a tournament between himself and the King of North Wales, and if Sir Lancelot would be there to help her father she would deliver him early the next morning.

"Fair maiden," said Lancelot, "tell me what is your father's name, and then I will give you an answer."

"My father is King Bagdemagus, who was defeated at the last tournament by three knights of King Arthur's Court."

"I know your father well for a noble king, and a good knight," said Lancelot, "and by my faith ye shall have my body ready to do your father and you service at that day."

So the maiden thanked him and bade him be ready very early the next morning, and she would come and deliver him. He was to take his armor, and his horse, shield and spear, and to ride to an abbey of white monks not ten miles away, where he was to stay, and there she would bring her father to him.

"All this shall be done," said Sir Lancelot, "as I am true knight."

The next morning the maiden came early, and found him ready. Then she took him through twelve locked doors, and brought him to his armor; and when he was well armed she led him to his own horse, and lightly he saddled him, and took a great spear in his hand, and rode forth.

"Fair damsel," he said, "I shall not fail you, by the grace of God."

So he rode into a great forest all that day, and could never find any highway, and at last the night fell on him.

The next day he came to the abbey, where the daughter of King Bagdemagus was waiting to receive him, and she gave him a glad welcome. In all haste she sent for her father, who was within twelve miles of the abbey, and before evening he arrived with a gallant company of knights. Sir Lancelot told the King how he had been betrayed, and how his nephew Sir Lionel had departed from him he knew not where; and how the King's daughter had delivered him out of prison—"therefore while I live I shall do her service, and all her kindred," he ended.

"Then am I sure of your help on this coming Tuesday?" said the King.

"Yea, sir," said Lancelot, "I shall not fail you, for so I have promised my lady, your daughter. But, sir, what knights are they of my lord Arthur's that were with the King of North Wales?"

The King replied that they were Sir Mador de la Porte, and Sir Mordred, and Sir Gahalatine, and against these three neither he nor his knights had any strength.

"Sir," said Lancelot, "as I hear say that the tournament shall be within three miles of this abbey, ye shall send unto me three knights of yours such as you trust, and look that the three knights have all white shields, and I also, and no painting on the shields. We four will come out of a little wood in the midst of both parties, and we will fall on the foremost of our enemies, and grieve them all we can; and thus it shall not be known what knight I am."

That night, which was the Sunday, they took their rest, and the next day King Bagdemagus departed; and he sent to Sir Lancelot the three knights with the four white shields.

THE MANOR BY THE FORD

On the Tuesday Sir Lancelot and the three knights from King Bagdemagus, with the white shields, lodged in a little leafy wood beside where the tournament would be held. And there were stands erected, so that lords and ladies could see, and give the prize.

Then came into the field the King of North Wales with eight score of helms, and the three knights of Arthur stood by themselves.

Then came into the field King Bagdemagus with four score helms. They put their spears in rest, and dashed at each other, and at the first encounter twelve knights of King Bagdemagus were slain, and six of the King of North Wales, and King Bagdemagus' party was driven far back.

With that came Sir Lancelot of the Lake, and he thrust with his spear in the thickest of the press, and knight after knight went down before him, and among the throng he smote down the King of North Wales. King Arthur's three knights saw this deed of Lancelot's, and each in turn attacked him, and each was vanquished.

After this he fought with twenty-eight knights, and overthrew every one of them, and then the knights of the King of North Wales would joust no more, and the prize was given to King Bagdemagus.

So each party departed to his own palace, and Sir Lancelot rode forth with King Bagdemagus to his Castle, where he had passing good cheer both with the King and his daughter, and they offered him great gifts.

On the morrow he took his leave, and told King Bagdemagus that he would go and seek his nephew Sir Lionel, who went from him when he was asleep. So he took his horse, and commended them all to God. And to the King's daughter he said:

"If ye have need anytime of my service, I pray you let me know, and I shall not fail you as I am true knight."

So Sir Lancelot departed, and by chance he came into the same forest where he was taken sleeping. And in the midst of a highway he met a damsel riding a white palfrey, and they each saluted the other.

"Fair damsel," said Sir Lancelot, "know ye in this country any adventures?"

"Sir Knight," said the damsel, "here are adventures near at hand, if thou darest prove them."

"Why should I not prove adventures?" said Sir Lancelot, "for that cause came I into the country."

"Well," said she, "thou seemest indeed to be a good knight, and if thou dare meet with a good knight I will bring thee where is the best and the mightiest that ever thou found, so thou wilt tell me what is thy name, and what knight thou art."

"To tell thee my name I am quite ready, truly it is Sir Lancelot of the Lake."

"Sir, thou art a well-seeming knight; here are adventures to suit thee. For hereby dwelleth a knight that will not be over-matched by any one I know, unless ye over-match him; his name is Sir Turquine. And, as I understand, he hath in his prison three score and four good knights of Arthur's Court, whom he hath won with his own hands. But when ye have done this day's work ye shall promise me as ye are a true knight to go with me and help me and other damsels that are distressed daily with a false knight."

"I will fulfil all your desire, damsel, so that you bring me to this knight."

So she brought him to the ford and to the tree where hung the basin.

Sir Lancelot let his horse drink, and then he beat with all his might on the basin with the butt of his spear, till at last the bottom fell out, but he saw nothing. He rode up and down in front of the gates of that manor for nearly half-an-hour; then he was aware of a great knight coming who drove a horse before him, and across the horse lay an armed knight, bound. As they came nearer and nearer Sir Lancelot thought he should know him, and then he saw it was Sir Gaheris, Gawaine's brother, a Knight of the Round Table.

By that time Sir Turquine had seen Lancelot, and they both gripped their spears.

"Now, fair knight," said Lancelot, "put that wounded knight off the horse, and let him rest awhile, and let us two prove our strength. For, as I am told, thou dost, and hast done, great despite and shame unto Knights of the Round Table; therefore, now defend thee!"

"If thou be of the Round Table I defy thee and all thy fellowship," said Sir Turquine.

"That is saying overmuch," said Sir Lancelot.

Then they put their spears in rest, and came together with their horses as fast as they could run, and each smote the other in the midst of their shields, so that the two horses' backs were broken. Both knights were astonished, and as soon as they could get clear of the horses they flung their shields in front of them, and drew their swords, and rushed together eagerly, so that neither shield nor armor could withstand their strokes. Within a little while they had both grim wounds, and thus it fared for two hours or more. Then at last they were both breathless, and stood leaning on their swords.

"Now, fellow," said Sir Turquine, "hold thy hand awhile, and tell me what I shall ask thee."

"Say on," said Lancelot.

"Thou art the biggest man that ever I met withal, and the most skilled, and like one knight that I hate above all other knights. If so be that thou art not he then I will willingly agree with thee, and for thy love I will deliver all the prisoners I have, who are three score and four, so thou wilt tell me thy name. And thou and I will be friends together and never fail, as long as I live."

"Well said," answered Sir Lancelot, "but since I may have thy friendship, what knight is he whom thou so hatest above all others?"

"Faithfully he is Sir Lancelot of the Lake, for he slew my brother at the Dolorous Tower, who was one of the best knights living. Therefore him I except, for may I once meet with him, the one of us shall make an end of the other, I swear a vow. And for Sir Lancelot's sake I have slain a hundred good knights, and as many have I maimed, and many have died in prison, and still I have three score and four. But all shall be delivered if thou wilt tell me thy name, so it be that thou are not Sir Lancelot."

"Now see I well," said Sir Lancelot, "that I might be such a man that I might have peace, and I might be such a man that there should be deadly war betwixt us. And now, Sir Knight, at thy request I desire that thou learn and know that I am Lancelot of the Lake, King Ban's son, of Benwick, and true Knight of the Table Round. And now I defy thee, do thy best!"

"Ah, Lancelot," said Turquine, "thou art most welcome to me that ever was knight, for we shall never part till the one of us be dead."

Then they hustled together like two wild bulls, rashing and lashing with their shields and swords. Thus they fought still two hours and more, and never would have rest. And Sir Turquine gave Sir Lancelot many wounds, so that all the ground there where they fought was bespeckled with blood. Then at the last Sir Turquine waxed faint, and gave somewhat aback, and bore his shield low for weariness. Sir Lancelot espied this, and leaped upon him fiercely, and got him by the beaver of his helmet and plucked him down on his knees. Then he quickly raised off his helm and smote his neck in sunder.

And when Sir Lancelot had done this, he went to the damsel, and said:

"Damsel, I am ready to go with you where you will have me, but I have no horse."

"Fair sir," said she, "take this wounded knight's horse, and send him to the Manor, and command him to deliver all the prisoners."

So Lancelot went to Gaheris, and prayed him not to be aggrieved at lending him his horse.

"Nay, fair lord," said Gaheris, "I will that ye take my horse at your own commandment, for ye have saved both me and my horse; and this day I say you are the best knight in the world, for you have slain here in my sight the mightiest man and the best knight, except you, that ever I saw. I pray you, sir, tell me your name."

"Sir, my name is Lancelot of the Lake, that ought to help you of right for King Arthur's sake, and in especial for my Lord Gawaine's sake, your own dear brother. And when you come within yonder Manor, I am sure you will find there many Knights of the Round Table, for I have seen many of their shields that I know on yonder tree. And among them are my two kinsmen's shields, Sir Ector de Maris, and Sir Lionel. Wherefore I pray you, greet them all from me, and say that I bid them take such treasure as they find in the Manor, and that in any case let my kinsmen go to the Court and wait till I come, for by the Feast of Pentecost, I purpose to be there; for at this time I must ride with this damsel to keep my promise."

So Sir Lancelot departed, and Sir Gaheris went into the Manor, and there he found a yeoman porter, keeping many keys. Sir Gaheris quickly threw the porter to the ground, and took the keys from him, and hastily he opened the prison door, and let out all the prisoners; and every man loosed each other's bonds.

When they saw Gaheris they all thanked him, for they saw he was wounded.

"Not so," said Gaheris, "it was Lancelot that slew your captor, I saw it with my own eyes. And he greeteth you all well, and prayeth you to hasten to Court; and as for Sir Lionel and Sir Ector de Maris, he prayeth you to wait for him at Court."

"That shall we not do," said the brothers, "we will find him, if we live."

"So shall I find him before I go to Court, as I am true knight," said Sir Kay.

Then all the knights sought the house where the armor was, and armed themselves, and every knight found his own horse, and all that belonged to him. And when this was done there came a forester with four horses laden with fat venison.

"Here is good meat for us for one meal," said Sir Kay, "for we have had no good repast for many a day."

So the venison was roasted, baked, and boiled, and after supper some of the knights abode there in the Manor all that night, but Sir Lionel and Ector de Maris and Sir Kay rode after Sir Lancelot to find him if they could.

HOW SIR LANCELOT SLEW TWO GIANTS

Sir Lancelot rode away with the damsel, as he had promised, to aid her against the wicked knight who robbed and distressed all ladies and gentlewomen.

"He doth shame unto the order of knighthood and contrary unto his oath," he said; "it is pity that he liveth. But, fair damsel, you shall ride on in front, and I will keep myself in covert, and if he trouble or distress you, I will rescue you, and teach him to be ruled as a knight."

So the maid rode gently along the highway.

Soon out of the wood came the wicked knight on horseback, and his page with him, and he took the damsel from her horse, and she cried out.

With that came Sir Lancelot as fast as he could.

"O thou false knight, and traitor unto knighthood!" he said. "Who taught thee to distress ladies and gentlewomen?"

When the knight heard this rebuke he made no answer, but drew his sword and rode at Sir Lancelot. Then Lancelot threw his spear from him, and drew out his sword, and struck him such a buffet on the helmet that he clave his head and neck to the throat.

"Now thou hast thy payment which thou hast long deserved, and that is truth," said the damsel. "For as Sir Turquine watched to destroy knights, so did this knight wait to destroy and distress ladies, damsels, and gentlewomen; and his name was Sir Peris of Forest Savage."

"Now, damsel," said Sir Lancelot, "will ye any more service of me?"

"Nay, sir, not at this time," she said, "but Christ preserve you wheresoever you ride or go! For the courtliest knight thou art, and meekest unto all ladies and gentlewomen that now liveth."

And so Sir Lancelot and she parted.

Then Sir Lancelot rode in a deep forest two days and more, and had hard lodging. On the third day he rode over a long bridge, and there suddenly started out on him a horrible churl, who smote his horse on the nose so that it turned away, and asked him why he rode over that bridge without his permission.

"Why should I not ride this way?" said Sir Lancelot.

"Thou shalt not choose," said the churl, and lashed at him with a great club shod with iron.

Then Sir Lancelot drew his sword and thrust the stroke aside, and cleft the villain's head.

At the end of the bridge was a fair village, and all the people, men and women, cried to Sir Lancelot:

"A worse deed for thyself didst thou never, for thou hast slain the chief porter of our Castle."

Sir Lancelot let them say what they would, and went straight into the Castle; and when he came there he alighted, and tied his horse to a ring on the wall. There he saw a fair green court, to this he went, for he thought it was a good place to fight in. And looking about he saw many people at the doors and windows, who said:

"Fair knight, thou are in evil luck!"

Soon there came upon him two great giants, well armed, all except the heads, and with two horrible clubs in their hands. Flinging his shield before him, Sir Lancelot turned

75

away the stroke of the one giant, and with his sword clave his head asunder. When his companion saw that, he ran away as if he were mad, for fear of the horrible strokes; but Lancelot ran after him with all his might, and smote him on the shoulder, and killed him.

Then Sir Lancelot went into the hall, and there came sixty ladies and damsels, who all knelt to him and thanked God and him for their deliverance.

"For, sir," said they, "most of us have been prisoners here seven years, and we have worked all manner of silk works for our meat, and we are all high-born gentlewomen. Blessed be the time, knight, that ever thou wert born, for thou hast done the noblest deed that ever knight did, and that we will bear record. We all pray thee to tell us thy name, that we may tell our friends who delivered us out of prison."

"Fair damsels," he said, "my name is Sir Lancelot of the Lake."

"Ah, sir," said they, "well mayst thou be he, for save thyself, as we deemed, there might never knight have the better of these two giants. Many good knights have assayed it, and here have ended, and many times have we wished for thee, for these two giants dreaded no knight but thee."

"Now you can say to your friends how and by whom you have been delivered," said Lancelot, "and greet them all from me. What treasure there is in this Castle I give it all to you, as reward for your grievance; and the lord that is owner of this Castle, I would that he receive it, as is right."

"The name of this Castle is Tintagel," said the ladies, "and for some time a duke had it, who was wedded to the fair Igraine. And after his death she married King Uther Pendragon, and Arthur was their son."

"Well," said Sir Lancelot, "I understand now to whom

this Castle belongs."

And so he commended them to God, and departed.

Then he mounted his horse, and rode into many wild and strange countries, and through many waters and valleys, and evil was he lodged. At last one night he happened by chance to come to a fair courtyard, and there he found an old gentlewoman who lodged him with a good will, and he had good cheer for himself and his horse. And when it was time, his host took him to a fair room over the gate, to go to bed. There Sir Lancelot unarmed him, and set his armor beside him, and went to bed, and quickly fell asleep.

Soon after, came one on horseback, and knocked at the gate in great haste. When Sir Lancelot heard this he arose, and looking out at the window, he saw by the moonlight three knights come riding after that one knight, and all three lashed on him at once with swords, and that one knight turned on them valiantly again, and defended himself.

"Truly," said Sir Lancelot, "yonder one knight shall I help, for it were shame to me to see three knights on one, and if he be slain, I am partner in his death."

Therewith he took his armor, and went out of the window, letting himself down by a sheet, to the four knights.

"Turn, you knights, unto me!" he cried aloud, "and leave your fighting with that knight."

Then they all left the other, who was Sir Kay, and turned to Sir Lancelot, and there began a great battle, for they all three alighted, and struck great strokes at Lancelot, and assailed him on every side. But when Sir Kay would have gone to Lancelot's help, the latter bade him let them fight him alone, so to please him, Sir Kay stood aside. And quickly then, in six strokes, Sir Lancelot had stricken them to the earth.

Then they all cried, "Sir Knight, we yield us unto you as a man of matchless might."

"As to that," said Sir Lancelot, "I will not take your yielding unto me, but if ye yield you unto Sir Kay the Steward, on that covenant I will save your lives, and not else."

"That were we loath to do, fair knight," they said, "for as for Sir Kay we chased him hither, and had overcome him, if you had not been here; therefore there is no reason why we should yield to him."

"As to that be well advised," said Lancelot, "for you can choose whether you shall die or live; but if you yield, it shall be to Sir Kay."

"Well," they answered, "as you have saved our lives, we will do as you command."

Then Lancelot bade them go to the Court of King Arthur on the coming Wednesday, and there yield them to Queen Guinevere, and put themselves in her grace and mercy, saying that Sir Kay had sent them to be her prisoners. And every knight swore faithfully upon his sword that he would do this. So Sir Lancelot suffered them to depart.

Then he knocked at the gate with the pommel of his sword, and therewith came his host, and in they entered, Sir Kay and he.

His host had heard nothing of the disturbance, and was surprised to see them. "Sir," he said, "I thought you were in your bed."

"So I was," said Sir Lancelot, "but I arose and leaped out of my window to help an old comrade of mine."

And so when they came near the light Sir Kay knew well that it was Sir Lancelot, and he knelt down and thanked him for all his kindness, because he had this second time helped him from death.

"Sir," said Lancelot, "I have done nothing but what I ought to do, so you are welcome; and here shall you repose, and take your rest."

When Sir Kay was unarmed he asked for some food, which was brought him, and he ate hungrily. After he had supped, he and Sir Lancelot went to their beds, and lodged together in one room.

In the morning Sir Lancelot rose early, and left Sir Kay sleeping; and Sir Lancelot took Sir Kay's armor and his shield, and armed himself; then he went to the stable and fetched his horse, and took leave of his host, and so he departed.

Then soon after Sir Kay arose and missed Sir Lancelot; and then he espied that he had taken his armor and his horse.

"Now by my faith I know well that he will grieve some of the Court of King Arthur; for knights will be bold to him, believing him to be me, and thus they will be deceived. And because of his armor and shield I am sure I shall ride in peace."

Then Sir Kay thanked his host, and soon departed.

CHAPEL PERILOUS
AND THE WICKED SORCERESS

SIR Lancelot, dressed in Sir Kay's armor, rode long in a great forest, and at last came to a flat country, full of fair rivers and meadows. Before him he saw a long bridge, and on it three pavilions of silk and sandal of different colors. Outside the pavilions hung three white shields on truncheons of spears, and great long spears stood upright by the pavilions and at every pavilion door stood a squire. Sir Lancelot passed by these and spoke no word.

"There goes the proud Sir Kay," said the knights to whom the pavilions belonged. "He thinks no knight so good as himself, but the contrary has often been proved."

"By my faith I will assay him, for all his pride," said one of the knights, "and you shall see how I speed." And arming himself he rode quickly after Lancelot, and challenged him to fight.

But Sir Lancelot smote him down, horse and man, and after that, when the other two knights came to their brother's assistance, he overthrew them, too. One of them started up with his head bleeding and came straight to Sir Lancelot.

"Now let be," said Lancelot, "I was not far from thee when thou wert made knight, Sir Raynold, and also I know thou art a good knight, and loath I should be to slay thee."

"Gramercy, as for your goodness," said Sir Raynold, "and I dare say as for me and my brethren we will not be loath to yield to you, if we knew your name; for well we know you are not Sir Kay."

"As for that, be it as it may," answered Lancelot, "for ye shall yield you unto Queen Guinevere. Look that ye be with her on Whitsunday, and yield you unto her as prisoners, and say that Sir Kay sent you unto her."

Then they swore it should be done, and Lancelot went on his way.

Riding on through the deep forest he saw there in a glade four knights standing under an oak. They were all of King Arthur's Court, and Sir Lancelot knew them well—they were Sagramour le Desirous, Sir Ector de Maris, Sir Gawaine, and Sir Uwaine. When they saw Lancelot they thought by his armor it was Sir Kay, so they agreed to fight him, to test his power. But Sir Lancelot rode at them all in turn, and overthrew them all, and went on his way smiling.

"What say ye of this deed," said Gawaine, "that one spear hath felled us four?"

"We commend him to the devil," said they all, "for he is a man of great might."

"Ye may well say that he is a man of might," said Gawaine, "for I dare lay my head it is Sir Lancelot, I know it by his riding. Let him go, for when we get to the Court then we shall know."

Sir Lancelot rode on for a great while in the deep forest, and at last he saw a black dog seeking about as if it were in the track of a hurt deer, and then he saw on the ground a trail of blood. So he rode after the dog, which kept looking back at him. It went through a great marsh, and Lancelot followed, and then he saw an old manor, and thither the dog ran across a bridge. Riding over the bridge, which was old and feeble, Sir Lancelot came presently to a great hall, and in the midst he saw lying a dead knight, a noble-looking man, and the dog licked his wounds.

Then there came out a lady weeping and wringing her hands.

"Oh, knight!" she said, "too much sorrow hast thou brought me!"

"Why say you so?" said Sir Lancelot. "I never did this knight any harm, for hither by track of blood this dog brought me. Therefore, fair lady, be not displeased with me, for I am full sorely grieved for your grievance."

"Truly, sir," she said, "I know it is not you who have slain my husband, for he who did the deed is sorely wounded, and never likely to recover—I shall make sure of that."

"What was your husband's name?" asked Sir Lancelot.

"Sir," said she, "his name was called Sir Gilbert, one of the best knights of the world, and I know not the name of him that hath slain him."

"Now God send you better comfort," said Sir Lancelot, and so he departed.

Then he went again into the forest, and there he met with a damsel who knew him well.

"Well found, my lord!" she said. "Now I require thee on thy knighthood help my brother, who is sore wounded. For this day he fought with Sir Gilbert, and slew him in plain battle, and there my brother was sorely wounded. And there is a lady, a sorceress, who dwells in a castle close by, and this day she told me my brother's wounds would never be whole till I could find a knight who would go into the Chapel Perilous, and there he would find a sword and a blood-stained cloth that Sir Gilbert was lapped in; and the sword and a piece of that cloth should heal my brother's wounds."

"This is a marvellous thing," said Lancelot, "but what is your brother's name?"

"Sir," said she, "his name is Sir Meliot de Logres."

"I am sorry for that," said Lancelot, "for he is a fellow of the Round Table, and to help him I will do all in my power."

"Then, sir," said the damsel, "follow this highway, and it will bring you to the Chapel Perilous. And here I shall bide till God send you here again; and unless you succeed I know no knight living who may achieve that adventure."

So Sir Lancelot departed, and when he came to the Chapel Perilous he alighted, and tied his horse to a little gate.

As soon as he was within the churchyard he saw many rich shields, turned upside down, and many of the shields Sir Lancelot had seen knights bear formerly.

Then he saw standing there by him thirty great knights, each taller by a yard than any he had ever seen, and all these grinned and gnashed at Sir Lancelot. When he saw their countenance he was in sore dread, so he put his shield before him, and took his sword in his hand, ready for battle; and all the knights were armed in black harness, ready with their shields and their swords drawn. But when Sir Lancelot would have passed through them, they scattered on every side, and gave him way, whereupon he waxed quite bold, and entered the chapel.

There he saw no light but a dim lamp burning, and then he was aware of a dead body covered with a cloth of silk.

Sir Lancelot stooped down and cut away a piece of the cloth, whereupon it seemed as if the earth quaked a little, at which he feared. Then he saw a fair sword in his hand and went out of the chapel.

As soon as ever he was in the chapel-yard all the knights spoke to him with a grim voice.

"Knight, Sir Lancelot, lay that sword from thee, or else thou shalt die."

"Whether I live or die," said Lancelot, "no big words will get it again, therefore fight for it, if you choose," and right so he passed through them.

Beyond the chapel-yard there met him a fair damsel, who said:

"Sir Lancelot, leave that sword behind thee, or thou wilt die for it."

"I shall not leave it, for any entreaties," said Lancelot.

"No," said she, "if thou didst leave that sword, thou wouldst never again see Queen Guinevere."

"Then I were a fool if I left it," said Lancelot.

"Now, gentle knight," said the damsel, "I require thee to kiss me but once."

"Nay," said Lancelot, "God forbid!"

"Well, sir," said she, "if thou hadst kissed me, all the days of thy life would have been done. But now, alas!" she said, "I have lost all my labor, for I ordained the chapel for thy sake. And now, Sir Lancelot, I tell thee I have loved thee these seven years, but no woman may have thy love but Queen Guinevere; since I might not rejoice to have thee alive, I had no greater joy in this world than to have thy body dead. Then would I have had it embalmed, and preserved, and so have kept it all the days of my life, and daily I would have kissed thee, in spite of Queen Guinevere."

"Ye say well," said Sir Lancelot. "God preserve me from thy subtle crafts!"

And therewith he took his horse, and departed from her.

And when Sir Lancelot departed she took such sorrow that she died within a fortnight; and her name was Hellawes, the sorceress, lady of the Castle Nigramous.

Sir Lancelot soon met with the damsel, Sir Meliot's sister, and when she saw him, she clapped her hands, and wept for joy, and then they rode to a castle near by where Sir Meliot lay.

Directly Sir Lancelot saw him he recognized him as one of Arthur's knights, but Sir Meliot was as pale as death from bleeding; then Lancelot sprang to him, and touched his wounds with Sir Gilbert's sword, and wiped them with a piece of the cloth in which Sir Gilbert had been wrapped, and immediately Sir Meliot was more well and strong than he had ever been in his life.

Then there was great joy between them, and they made Sir Lancelot all the cheer they could. When Sir Lancelot took his leave in the morning, he bade Sir Meliot hie to the Court of King Arthur, for it drew nigh to the Feast of Pentecost, and there by the grace of God he would find him.

THE DECEIT OF THE FALCON

In this way Sir Lancelot rode through many strange countries, over marshes and valleys, till by fortune he came to a fair castle, and as he passed beyond the castle he thought he heard two bells ring. Then he was aware of a falcon that came flying over his head to a high elm; long lines were about her feet, and as she flew into the elm to take her perch the lines caught in a bough. When she would have taken her flight, she hung by the legs fast, and Sir Lancelot saw how she hung, and was sorry for the beautiful peregrine falcon.

Meanwhile a lady came out of the castle, and cried:

"O, Lancelot, Lancelot, as thou are flower of all knights, help me to get my hawk, for if my hawk be lost, my lord will destroy me. For I kept the hawk, and she slipped from me, and if my husband know it he is so hasty he will slay me."

"What is your husband's name?" said Lancelot.

"Sir," she said, "his name is Sir Phelot, a knight of the King of North Wales."

"Well, fair lady, since you know my name and require me of knighthood to help you, I will do what I can to get your hawk; and yet truly I am an ill climber, and the tree is passing high, and there are few boughs to help me."

Therewith Sir Lancelot alighted, and tied his horse to the

same tree, and begged the lady to help him off with his armor. And when he was unarmed he put off all his clothes to his shirt and breeches, and with might and skill he climbed up to the falcon, and tied the lines to a great, rotten branch, and threw it and the falcon down.

The lady at once took hold of the falcon. Then suddenly out of the grove came Sir Phelot, her husband, all armed, and with his naked sword in his hand.

"O knight, Lancelot, now have I found thee as I would," he said, and stood at the bole of the tree to slay him.

"Ah, lady," said Sir Lancelot, "why have you betrayed me?"

"She has only done as I commanded her," said Sir Phelot, "and therefore there is no help for it but thine hour is come that thou must die."

"That were shame unto thee," said Sir Lancelot, "thou an armed knight to slay an unarmed man by treason."

"Thou gettest no other grave," said Sir Phelot, "therefore help thyself if thou canst."

"Truly," said Lancelot, "that shall be thy shame; but since thou wilt do no other, take my armor with thee, and hang my sword upon a bough that I may get it, and then do thy best to slay me, if thou canst."

"Nay, nay," said Sir Phelot, "for I know thee better than thou thinkest, therefore thou gettest no weapon, if I can keep thee from it."

"Alas!" said Sir Lancelot, "that ever a knight should die weaponless!"

Then he looked above him, and under him, and over his head he saw a great branch, leafless, with other branches growing out of it, and this he broke off from the trunk. Then he came lower, and marked how his own horse stood, and suddenly he leaped on the farther side of the horse from the knight. Sir Phelot lashed at him eagerly, thinking to have slain him; but Sir Lancelot thrust away the stroke with the branch, and smote him on the side of the head, so that he fell in a swoon to the ground. Then Lancelot took Sir Phelot's sword out of his hand, and struck off his head.

"Alas, why hast thou slain my husband," cried the lady.

"I am not to blame," said Sir Lancelot, "for with falsehood ye would have slain me by treason, and now it has fallen on you both."

Then the lady swooned as though she would die.

Sir Lancelot got all his armor as well as he could, and put it on him, for he dreaded further attack, because the knight's castle was so near. As quickly as possible he took his horse and departed, thanking God that he had escaped that adventure.

Two days before the Feast of Pentecost he went home, and the King and all the Court rejoiced greatly at his coming. When the four knights with whom he had fought in the wood saw Sir Lancelot in Kay's armor they knew well it was he who had smote them all down with one spear, and there was much laughing and smiling among them. And now all the knights whom Sir Turquine had kept as prisoners came trooping home, and they all honored and worshipped Sir Lancelot. When Sir Gaheris heard him speak, he said, "I saw all the battle, from the beginning to the end," and there he told King Arthur how it was, and how Sir Turquine was the strongest knight that ever he saw, except Sir Lancelot; and there were nearly three score knights who bore him record.

Then Sir Kay told the King how Sir Lancelot had rescued him when he would have been slain in the night, outside the manor where Lancelot was lodging; and how he made the knights yield to Sir Kay, and not to himself. And there the knights were, all three, and bare record.

"And by my faith," said Sir Kay, "because Sir Lancelot took my harness and left me his, I rode in good peace, and no man would touch me."

Then also came the three knights who fought with Lancelot at the long bridge, and they would have yielded them at the Court to Sir Kay; but Sir Kay refused them, and said he never fought with them.

"But I will ease your hearts," he said, "yonder is Sir Lancelot, who overcame you."

When they knew that, they were glad.

Then Sir Meliot de Logres came home, and told King Arthur how Sir Lancelot had saved him from death by facing the unknown dangers, and the evil spells in the Chapel Perilous.

And all his deeds were known—how four Queens, sorceresses, had him in prison, and how he was delivered by King Bagdemagus' daughter. Also there were told all the great deeds of arms that Sir Lancelot did in the tournament betwixt the two kings, that is to say, the King of North Wales and King Bagdemagus.

So at that time Sir Lancelot had the greatest name of any knight of the world, and he was the most honored, both by high and low.

THE BOY OF THE KITCHEN

THE THREE GIFTS

ONCE when King Arthur held his Round Table in its full glory, it happened that he commanded that the high Feast of Pentecost should be held at a castle in a city which in those days was called Kink-Kenadon, upon the sands that marched next Wales. The King had always a special custom at the Feast of Pentecost—namely, that he would not sit down to meat until he had heard of, or seen, a great marvel. And because of this custom all manners of strange adventures came before Arthur at that feast more than at any other festival in the year.

On this day of Pentecost, a little before noon, Sir Gawaine espied from a window three men on horseback and a dwarf on foot. The three men alighted, and the dwarf kept their horses, and one of the three men was taller than the other two by a foot and a half.

Then Sir Gawaine went to the King, and said:

"Sir, go to your meat, for here at hand come strange adventures."

So Arthur went to meat with many other Kings, and all the Knights of the Round Table were there, save those who were prisoners or who had been slain in battle. For at the high feast the whole number of one hundred and fifty should always be present, for then was the Round Table fully complete.

Then came into the hall two men, richly clad, with the goodliest young man and the fairest that they had ever seen leaning on their shoulders, as if he could not go by himself. He was large and tall, and broad in the shoulders, handsome of face, and had the largest and most beautiful hands that ever a man saw.

As soon as King Arthur saw him, place and room were made, and the two strange men went with him right up to the high dais without saying a word.

Then this great young man pulled himself back, and easily stretched up straight, saying:

"King Arthur, God bless you and all your fair fellowship, and in especial the fellowship of the Round Table. And for this cause I am come hither, to pray you and require you to give me three gifts, and they shall not be unreasonably asked, but such as ye may worshipfully and honorably grant to me, at no great hurt or loss. The first gift I will ask now, and the other two gifts I will ask this day twelvemonth, wheresoever you hold your high feast."

"Now ask," said Arthur, "and ye shall have your asking."

"Sir, this is my position for this feast—that you will give me meat and drink sufficient for this twelvemonth, and at that day I will ask my other two gifts."

"My fair son," said Arthur, "ask better, I counsel thee, for this is but a simple asking; my heart assures me greatly that thou art come of men of worship, and much my judgment fails me unless thou prove a man of right good worship."

"Sir," said the young man, "let that be as it may, I have asked that which I will ask."

"Well," said the King, "you shall have meat and drink enough, I never forbade that to anyone, either my friend or my foe. But what is your name?"

"I cannot tell you."

"That is a marvel, that thou knowest not thy name," said the King. "Thou art the goodliest young man that ever I saw." And he went to Sir Kay the Steward, and charged him that he should give the stranger lad all manner of meat and drinks of the best, and that he should be provided for in every way as if he were a lord's son.

"There is little need to spend so much on him," said Sir Kay, "for I dare undertake he is of mean birth, and will never make a man; if he had come of gentle folk he would have asked of you horse and armor, but he asks according to his own nature. And since he hath no name I will give him one—*Beau-mains*, that is, 'Fair-hands'—and I will bring him into the kitchen, and there he shall have rich broth every day, so that by the twelve months' end he shall be as fat as a pork hog."

So the two strange men departed, leaving the tall lad to Sir Kay, who scorned and mocked him.

Sir Gawaine and Sir Lancelot were very angry at the way in which Sir Kay treated the lad, but the steward persisted he would never make a man of worship, because he only desired meat and drink. He bade him get a place and sit down to meat, so Beaumains went to the hall door, and sat down among the serving boys and lads, and there he ate sadly.

After the meal Sir Lancelot bade him come to his chamber, and there he should have meat and drink enough, and Sir Gawaine offered the same. But he refused them both. He would do nothing but what Sir Kay commanded him.

As for Sir Gawaine, it was natural he should offer Beaumains lodging, with meat and drink, for the boy was nearer kin to him than he guessed. But what Sir Lancelot did was of his great gentleness and courtesy.

So Beaumains was put into the kitchen, and lay nightly as the boys of the kitchen did. And he endured it all a twelvemonth, and never displeased man or child, but was always meek and mild. But if ever there were any jousting of knights, he would see it, if he could. Sir Lancelot and Sir Gawaine often gave him gold to spend, and clothes. Wherever there were any feats of skill and strength, there Beaumains would be, and no one could cast bar or stone as he did, by two yards. Then Sir Kay would say:

"How like you my boy of the kitchen?"

So time passed till the Feast of Pentecost came round again. And that year the King held it at Carleon in most royal fashion. But on Whitsunday, according to his custom, he would eat no meat until he heard some adventure. Then there came a squire to the King, and said, "Sir, you may go to meat, for here cometh a damsel with some strange adventures," whereupon the King was glad, and sat down.

At that moment a damsel came into the hall, and saluted the King, and prayed succor of him.

"For whom?" said the King. "What is the adventure?"

"Sir," said she, "I have a lady of great worship and renown, and she is beseiged by a tyrant, so that she cannot get out of her castle. And because in this your Court are the noblest knights of the world, I come to pray succor of you."

"What is your lady called, and where dwelleth she? And who is he, and what is his name, who hath besieged her?"

"Sir King," said the damsel, "as for my lady's name, that ye shall not know from me at present, but on my word she is a lady of great worship, and of many lands. As for the tyrant who besieges her and destroys her lands, he is called the Red Knight of the Red Lawns."

"I know him not," said the King.

"Sir," said Gawaine, "I know him well, for he is one of the most dangerous knights in the world. Men say that he hath seven men's strength, and from him I escaped once full hardly with my life."

"Fair damsel," said the King, "there be knights here who would do their utmost to rescue your lady, but because you will not tell her name, nor where she dwells, therefore by my will none of my knights that are now here shall go with you."

"Then I must seek further," said the damsel.

As she said these words Beaumains came before the King, and spoke.

"Sir King, God thank you, I have been these twelve months in your kitchen, and have had my full sustenance, and now I will ask my two gifts that are left."

"Ask," said the King.

"Sir, these shall be my two gifts. First, that you will grant me to have this adventure of the damsel, for it belongs to me."

"Thou shalt have it," said the King, "I grant it thee."

"Then sir, this is the other gift, that thou shalt bid Lancelot of the Lake make me knight, for of him I will be made knight, or else of none. Therefore when I am gone I pray you let him ride after me, and make me knight when I require him."

"All this shall be done," said the King.

"Fie on thee!" said the damsel. "Shall I have none but one that is your kitchen page?"

Then she took her horse, in great wrath, and departed.

THE SCORNFUL DAMSEL

THEN came a messenger to Beaumains and told him that his horse and armor had come, and that the dwarf was there with everything he needed, in the richest style. All the Court marvelled greatly where such beautiful array came from. When he was armed there were few indeed who looked so goodly as he.

Thus he came into the hall, and took his leave of King Arthur, and Sir Gawaine, and Sir Lancelot; and begging the latter to follow after him, he departed, and rode after the damsel.

Many followed him to behold how well he was horsed, and trapped in cloth of gold, but he had neither shield nor spear. Then Sir Kay said all openly in the hall:

"I will ride after my boy of the kitchen, to find out whether he will know me for his better."

Sir Lancelot and Sir Gawaine said, "Ye had best abide at home." But Sir Kay made ready and took horse and spear, and rode after Beaumains.

Just as Beaumains overtook the damsel, up came Sir Kay.

"Beaumains! What, sir, do you not know me?" he cried.

Beaumains turned his horse, and knew it was Sir Kay, who had always treated him with scorn.

"Yes," he said, "I know you for an ungentle knight of the Court, and therefore, beware of me."

Therewith Sir Kay put spear in rest and ran straight at

him, and Beaumains, sword in hand, came equally fast
against Sir Kay. With his sword he dashed away Sir Kay's
spear, and thrust him in the side, so that he fell down as if
he had been dead. Then Beaumains alighted and took Sir
Kay's shield and spear, and bidding his dwarf mount Sir
Kay's horse, he sprang upon his own horse and rode away.

Sir Lancelot saw all that had happened, and so did the
damsel, and Sir Lancelot having by this time come up to
them, Beaumains offered to joust with him.

They came together so fiercely that each bore down the
other to the earth, and sorely were they bruised. Then
Lancelot arose, and helped Beaumains to get free from his
horse. Throwing his shield from him, Beaumains offered
to fight with Sir Lancelot on foot. They rushed together like
boars tracing, racing, and foining, for the whole of an hour,
and Sir Lancelot marvelled at the strength of Beaumains,
for he fought more like a giant than a knight, and his fighting was steady and very dangerous.

Sir Lancelot had such ado to hold his own that he dreaded
being disgraced.

"Beaumains," he said, "fight not so sore, your quarrel and
mine is not so great but we may leave off."

"Truly that is truth," said Beaumains, "but it doth me good
to feel your might; and yet, my lord, I did not show my
utmost strength."

"Well," said Sir Lancelot, "I swear to you that I had as
much as I could do to save myself from you unashamed,
therefore have no doubt of any earthly knight."

"Do you hope that I may ever at any time stand a proved
knight?" said Beaumains.

"Yes," said Lancelot, "do as you have done, and I will be
your warrant."

"Then I pray you give me the order of knighthood."

"Well, you must tell me your name and of what kin you are born."

"Sir, if you will not reveal it, I will."

"Nay," said Sir Lancelot, "and that I promise you by the faith of my body, until it be openly known."

"Then, sir, my name is Gareth," said Beaumains, "and I am the brother of Sir Gawaine, by the same father and mother."

"Now I am more than ever rejoiced," said Lancelot, "for I always thought you must be of noble race, and that you came not to the Court either for meat or drink."

And then Sir Lancelot gave him the order of knighthood.

After this, Lancelot left Beaumains, and went to Sir Kay, and had him carried home on his shield. Sir Kay barely escaped with his life, and all men scorned him, and in especial Sir Gawaine; and Sir Lancelot said it was not his part to rebuke any young man, when he knew little of what birth he came, and for what cause he came to Court.

In the meanwhile Beaumains had overtaken the damsel, but as soon as he came near she cried rudely:

"What are you doing here? You smell of the kitchen! Your clothes reek of the grease and tallow that you gained in King Arthur's kitchen. Do you suppose I will accept you because of yonder knight you killed? Nay, truly, for you slew him by ill chance, and cowardly. Therefore turn back, vile kitchen page! I know you well, for Sir Kay named you Beaumains. What are you but a clumsy fellow, and a turner of spits, and a ladle-washer."

"Damsel," replied Beaumains, "say to me what you will; I will not go from you, whatsoever you say, for I have undertaken to King Arthur to achieve your adventure. I shall finish it to the end, or I shall die for it."

"Fie on thee, kitchen knave! Will you finish my adventure? You will meet one whom, for all the broth that ever you supped, you would not once look in the face."

"I'll try," said Beaumains.

As they rode thus in the forest there came a man flying as fast as he could.

"O, lord," he said, "help me, for hard by in a glade are six robbers who have taken my lord and bound him; I am afraid lest they slay him."

"Take me there," said Beaumains.

So they went together till they came to where the knight was bound, and then Sir Beaumains rode at the robbers, and struck one unto death, and then another, and at the third stroke he slew the third robber; and then the other three fled. Beaumains rode after them and overtook them, whereupon they all assailed him hard, but at last he slew them, and returned and unbound the knight.

The knight thanked him, and prayed him to ride with him to his Castle a little way off, and he would reward him honorably for his good deeds.

"Sir," said Beaumains, "I will have no reward. This day I was made knight of noble Sir Lancelot, and therefore I will have no reward, except God reward me. And also I must follow this damsel."

But when he came near she bade him ride at a distance.

"You smell of the kitchen!" she said scornfully. "Do you think I am glad to have you? For this deed you have done is nothing but chance. You shall soon see a sight that will make you turn again, and that briskly!"

Then the same knight who had been rescued from the robbers rode after the damsel, and begged her to lodge with him that evening. And because it was near night the damsel rode with him to his Castle, and there they were made very welcome.

At supper the knight placed Beaumains above the damsel.

"Fie, fie, Sir Knight!" she said. "You are uncourteous to set a kitchen page above me! He is better fitting to kill a pig than to sit above a lady of high parentage."

The knight was ashamed at her rude words, and taking Beaumains he placed him at a side-table, and sat down himself beside him.

They had good cheer, and rested well that night.

THE BLACK KNIGHT OF THE BLACK LAWNS

On the morrow the damsel and Beaumains, thanking the knight, took their leave, and rode on their way until they came to a great forest. Here there was a great river, and but one passage, and two knights were ready on the further side to stop their crossing.

"What sayest thou?" said the damsel. "Wilt thou match yonder knights, or turn again?"

"Nay," said Sir Beaumains, "I will not turn again if they were six more."

Thereupon he rushed into the water, and one of the knights did the same. They fought in the midst of the river, and Beaumains smote the knight on the helm, so that he fell down into the water and was drowned. Then Beaumains spurred his horse to the further side of the river, where the other knight fell upon him and brake his spear, and so they drew their swords and fought long together. But at last Beaumains clave his head and his helm down to the shoulders.

Then he went back to the damsel and bade her ride forth on her way.

"Alas," she said, "that even a kitchen page should have the fortune to destroy two such doughty knights! Thou imaginest thou has done valiantly! That is not so; as for the first knight, his horse stumbled, and there he was drowned in the water,—it was never by thy strength nor thy might. And the last knight, by mishap thou camest behind him, and by evil luck thou slewest him."

"Damsel," said Beaumains, "you may say what you will, but with whomsoever I have to do I trust to God to vanquish him before he departs, and therefore I reck not what you say, if only I may reach your lady."

"Fie, fie, kitchen knave! Thou shalt see knights who shall abate thy boast!"

"Fair damsel, give me goodly language, and then I mind nothing; for what knights soever they be I care not, neither do I fear them."

"I say it for thine own sake," she said, "that thou mayst yet turn back with triumph; for if thou follow me thou art but slain, for I see that all thou ever dost is but by misadventure, and not by prowess of thy hands."

"Well, damsel, you may say what you will, but wheresoever you go, I will follow you."

So Beaumains rode with the lady until evensong time, and ever she chid him and would not rest. Then they came to a black lawn, where there was a black hawthorn; thereon hung a black banner, and on the other side hung a black shield; by the tree stood a black spear, great and long, and a great black horse covered with silk, and a black stone fast by.

There sat a knight all armed in black harness, and his name was the Knight of the Black Lawn.

When the damsel saw the knight, she bade Beaumains flee down the valley, for the black horse was not saddled.

"Thanks," said Beaumains, "for always ye would have me a coward."

With that the Black Knight, when she came near him, spoke and said:

"Damsel, have ye brought this knight of King Arthur to be your champion?"

"Nay, fair knight," said she, "this is but a kitchen knave who was fed in King Arthur's kitchen for alms."

"Why cometh he in such array?" said the knight. "It is a shame that he beareth you company."

"Sir, I cannot be delivered from him," she said, "for with me he rideth, in spite of all I can do. Would that you would put him from me, or else slay him if you can, for he is an unhappy knave, and unhappily he hath done this day. Through mishap I saw him slay two knights at the passage of the water; and other deeds he did before, right marvellous, and through ill fortune."

"It astonishes me that any man who is of worship will have to do with him," said the knight.

"They know him not," replied the damsel, "and because he rideth with me they think he is some man of high birth."

"That may be," said the Black Knight. "Howbeit as ye say he is no man of worship, he is a right goodly person, and full like to be a strong man. But thus much I will grant you," he continued; "I shall put him down on foot, and his horse and his harness he shall leave with me, for it were a shame to me to do him any more harm."

When Sir Beaumains heard him say this, he said:

"Sir Knight, thou art full liberal of my horse and my harness. I let thee know it cost thee nothing, and whether it liketh thee or no, this lawn will I pass, in spite of thee. And horse or harness gettest thou none of me unless thou win them with thy hands; and therefore let see what thou canst do!"

"Sayst thou that?" said the Black Knight. "Now yield thy lady from thee, for it beseemeth never a kitchen page to ride with such a lady."

"Thou liest," said Beaumains; "I am gentleman born, and of more high lineage than thou, and that I will prove on thy body."

Then in great wrath they drew apart their horses, and came together as if it had been thunder; and the Black Knight's spear broke, and Beaumains thrust him through both his sides, and therewith his spear broke, and the truncheon was left still in his side. Nevertheless the Black Knight drew his sword, and smote many eager strokes and of great might, and hurt Beaumains full sore. But at the last, within an hour and a half, the Black Knight fell down off his horse in a swoon, and there he died.

Beaumains seeing him so well horsed and armed, alighted, and armed himself in his armor, and taking his horse he rode after the damsel. When she saw him come near she cried:

"Away, kitchen knave, out of the wind, for the smell of thy greasy clothes grieveth me! Alas," she said, "that ever such a knave as thou art should by mishap slay so good a knight as thou hast done, but all this is thy evil luck! But hereby is one who shall pay thee all thy payment, and therefore still I counsel thee—flee!"

"It may happen me to be beaten or slain," said Beaumains, "but I warn you, fair damsel, I will not flee away nor leave your company for all that ye can say; ye are for ever declaring they will kill me or beat me, but howsoever it happeneth, I escape, and they lie on the ground. And therefore it were good for you to hold you still, thus all day rebuking me, for I will not go away till I see the very end of this journey, unless I am slain, or truly beaten. Therefore ride on your way, for follow you I will, whatsoever happen."

THE GREEN KNIGHT

As Beaumains and the damsel rode together they saw a knight come driving by them all in green, both his horse and his harness; and when he came near the damsel he asked her, "Is that my brother the Black Knight that ye have brought with you?"

"Nay, nay," said she, "this unhappy kitchen knave hath slain your brother through evil chance."

"Alas," said the Green Knight, "it is great pity that so noble a knight as he was should so unhappily be slain, and above all by a knave's hand, as ye say he is. Ah, traitor, ye shall die for slaying of my brother; he was a full noble knight, and his name was Sir Pecard."

"I defy thee," said Beaumains, "for I let thee know I slew him knightly, and not shamefully."

Therewith the Green Knight rode to a horn, which was green, and which hung on a thorn tree; and he blew three deadly notes, and there came two damsels, who quickly armed him. Then he took a great horse, and a green shield and a green spear. Beaumains and the Green Knight charged with all their might, and their spears broke up to their hands. Then they drew their swords, and gave many sad strokes, and each of them sorely wounded the other. And at the last Beaumains' horse struck the Green Knight's upon the side and it fell to the earth.

The Green Knight lightly leaped clear of his horse, and prepared to fight on foot, and Beaumains seeing this, also alighted, and they rushed together like two mighty champions, and long was the battle. Then the scornful damsel came near and began to taunt the Black Knight's brother.

"My lord the Green Knight, why for shame stand ye so long fighting with the kitchen knave? Alas, it is shame that ever ye were made knight, to see such a lad match such a knight, as if the weed overgrew the corn."

At this the Green Knight was ashamed and therewithal he gave a mighty stroke, and clave Beaumains' shield through. When Beaumains saw his shield cloven asunder he was vexed at that stroke, and at the damsel's language, and he gave the Green Knight such a buffet on the helm that he fell on his knees; and thus suddenly Beaumains pulled him upon the ground grovelling.

Then the Green Knight cried him mercy, and yielded him to Sir Beaumains, and prayed him to slay him not.

"All is in vain," said Beaumains, "for thou shalt die, unless this damsel that came with me pray me to save thy life."

Therewith he unlaced his helm as if he would slay him.

"Fie upon thee, false kitchen page!" cried the damsel, "I will never pray thee to save his life, for I never will be so much in thy power."

"Then he shall die," said Beaumains.

"Thou wilt never be so bold as to kill him, thou knave!" said the damsel.

"Alas," said the Green Knight, "suffer me not to die, for a fair word may save me. Gentle knight, save my life, and I will forgive thee the death of my brother, and for ever become thy man; and thirty knights that follow me shall for ever do you service."

"Now in the fiend's name that such a low kitchen knave should have thee and thirty knights' service!" said the damsel.

"Sir Knight," said Beaumains, "all this availeth thee not unless my damsel speak with me for thy life." And therewithal he made a semblance of slaying him.

"Let be, thee knave," said the damsel, "slay him not, for if thou do, thou shalt repent it."

"Damsel," said Beaumains, "your charge is to me a pleasure, and at your commandment his life shall be saved, and not else." Then he said, "Sir Knight with the green arms, I release thee at this damsel's request, for I will not make her wroth; I will fulfil all that she chargeth me."

Then the Green Knight knelt down and did him homage with his sword.

Then said the damsel:

"I am sorry, Green Knight, for your damage, and for your brother's death, the Black Knight, for of your help I have great need, for I sorely dread to pass this forest."

"Nay, dread not," said the Green Knight, "for ye shall lodge with me this night, and tomorrow I will help you through the forest."

So they took their horses and rode to his Manor, which was hard by.

The damsel never ceased from rebuking Beaumains, and when they reached the Manor she would not suffer him to sit at her table, so the Green Knight took him and set him at a side-table.

"I marvel," he said to the damsel, "why ye rebuke this noble knight as ye do, for I warn you, damsel, he is a full noble knight, and I know no knight able to match him; therefore ye do great wrong to rebuke him, for he shall do you right good service. Whatsoever he maketh himself out, ye shall prove at the end that he is come of noble blood, and of king's lineage."

"Fie, fie," said the damsel, "it is shame of you to say such honor of him."

"Truly," said the Green Knight, "it were shame of me to say of him any dishonor, for he hath proved himself a better knight than I am, yet have I met with many knights in my day, and never before this time have I found any knight his match."

So they went to rest, and all that night the Green Knight commanded thirty knights privily to watch Beaumains, to shield him from treason.

On the morrow they all arose, and having said their prayers, and broken their fast, they took their horses and rode on their way. The Green Knight conveyed them through the forest, and there he said:

"My lord Beaumains, I and these thirty knights shall be always at your summons, both early and late, at your calling, and wherever ye send us."

"It is well said," answered Beaumains. "When I call upon you, ye must yield you unto King Arthur, and all your knights."

"If ye so command us we shall be ready at all times," said the Green Knight.

"Fie, fie upon thee," cried the damsel, "that any good knights should be obedient to a kitchen knave!"

So the Green Knight departed.

"Why followest thou me, thou kitchen boy?" said the damsel rudely to Beaumains. "Cast away thy shield and thy spear, and flee away, I still counsel thee betimes, or thou shalt say right soon, 'Alas!' For wert thou brave as ever was Wade, or Lancelot, Tristram, or the Good knight Sir Lamorak, thou shalt not cross a pass here that is called the Pass Perilous."

"Damsel," said Beaumains, "he that is afeard, let him flee, for it were shame to turn back since I have ridden so long with you."

"Well," said the damsel, "you will soon, whether you wish it or not."

THE SCORNFUL DAMSEL GROWS KIND

WITHIN a little while they saw a tower as white as snow, having a double moat, and the parapets of the walls well provided with holes for hurling stones or pouring molten lead on the heads of any foes who might besiege it. Over the tower gate hung fifty shields of divers colors, and under the tower was a fair meadow. In the meadow were many knights and squires looking after scaffolds and pavilions, for on the morrow was to be a great tournament there.

The lord of the Castle was called the Red Knight, and he was a brother of the Black Knight and the Green Knight.

When he saw Beaumains, he came forth to fight with him, but after a furious struggle Beaumains vanquished him. He declared he would only spare his life at the request of the scornful damsel, so unwillingly she had to beg mercy for him. Then the Red Knight did homage to Sir Beaumains, and offered him his fealty at all times, he and his three score knights, to do him service and bidding whensoever and wheresoever he commanded.

That night Beaumains and the damsel lodged in the Castle of the Red Knight, and the next morning they went on their way.

But all this time the scornful damsel kept scolding and rebuking Beaumains in the rudest manner.

"Damsel," said Beaumains, "you are uncourteous to rebuke me as you do, for it seems to me I have done you good service; you keep on threatening me I shall be beaten by knights whom we meet, but ever, for all your boast, they lie in the dust, or in the mire; therefore, I pray you, rebuke me no more. When you see me beaten or yielding as recreant, then you may bid me go from you in disgrace; but first I let you know I will not depart from you, for I were worse than fool if I went when all the time I am winning honor."

"Well," said she, "right soon thou shalt meet a knight who will pay thee all thy wages, for he is the man of greatest renown in the world, except King Arthur."

"I wish nothing better," said Beaumains. "The more renowned he is, the more it shall be to my renown to have to do with him."

Then they were soon aware of a rich and beautiful city before them, and between them and the city for the space of a mile and a half stretched a fair meadow that seemed newly mown, and therein were many pavilions, splendid to see.

"Lo," said the damsel, "yonder is a lord who owneth yonder city, and it is his custom when the weather is fair to live in this meadow to joust and tourney; and he has always about him five hundred knights and gentlemen of arms, and there are all manner of games that any gentleman can devise."

"I would fain see that goodly lord," said Beaumains.

"Thou shalt see him in time enough," said the damsel; and just then, as they rode near she espied the pavilion where he was. "Lo," said she, "seest thou yonder pavilion that is of the color of Inde—dark blue? and everything that is about, men and women, and horses with trappings, shields and spears, all the color of Inde? His name is Sir Persant of Inde, the lordliest knight that ever thou lookedst on."

"It may well be," said Beaumains, "but be he never so stout a knight, in this field I shall abide till I see him under his shield."

"Ah, fool, thou hadst better flee betimes."

"Why?" said Beaumains. "If he be such a knight as ye make him, he will not set upon me with all his men, or with his five hundred knights. For if there come no more but one at a time, I shall not fail him, while my life lasteth."

"Fie, fie," said the damsel, "that ever a kitchen knave should utter such a boast!"

"Damsel," he said, "ye are to blame thus to rebuke me, for I would rather fight five battles than thus to be rebuked. Let him come, and then let him do his worst."

"Sir," she said, "I marvel of what kin thou art come; boldly thou speakest, and boldly hast thou done, that have I seen. Therefore I pray thee save thyself if thou canst, for thy horse and thou have had great travail, and I dread we stay over long from the siege, for it is but seven miles hence. And we are past all perilous passages, save only this passage; and here I sorely dread lest ye shall catch some hurt. Therefore I would you were hence, that you may not be bruised by this strong knight. But I tell you, this Sir Persant of Inde is nothing of might nor strength to the knight who laid the siege against my lady."

"As for that," said Beaumains, "be it as it may, for since I have come so nigh this knight I will prove his might before I depart from him, else I shall be shamed if I now withdraw. Therefore, damsel, doubt not that by the grace of God I shall so deal with this knight that within two hours after noon I shall be free from him, and then we shall come to the siege by daylight."

"Oh, indeed I marvel what manner of man you be," said the damsel, "for it cannot be otherwise than that ye come of noble blood, for so rude and shamefully did never woman rule a knight as I have done you, and ever courteously ye have suffered me, and that never came but of gentle blood."

"Damsel," said Beaumains, "a knight can do little that cannot suffer a woman. Whatsoever ye said to me I took no heed to your words, for the more you said, the more you angered me, and my wrath I wreaked upon those with whom I had to do withal. Therefore all the unseemly words you spoke furthered me in my battle, and caused me to resolve to show and prove myself what in the end I was; for peradventure, though I had meat in King Arthur's kitchen, yet I might have had meat enough in other places. But all this I did to prove and assay my friends, and that shall be known another day. Whether I be a gentleman born or none, fair damsel, I have done you gentleman's service, and peradventure better service will I yet do before I depart from you."

"Alas," she said, "fair Beaumains, forgive me all I have missaid or done against thee."

"With all my heart I forgive it you," he said, "for you did nothing but as you should do, for all your evil words pleased me. And, damsel, since you speak thus fairly to me, know well it gladdens my heart greatly, and now it seems to me there is no knight living but I am able enough for him."

By this time Sir Persant of Inde had espied them as they hovered in the field, and knightly sent to ask whether they came in war or peace. To this Beaumains replied that was exactly as Sir Persant pleased, whereupon Sir Persant said he would fight with him to the uttermost. So he armed himself and rode against him. Long and fierce was the encounter, but in the end Beaumains was the victor; Sir Persant surrendered and asked for mercy. The damsel, too, came and prayed for his life, which Beaumains granted right willingly, "For it were pity this noble knight should die," he said.

Then Sir Persant knew it was Beaumains who slew his brother the Black Knight, at the black thorn, and who had also overcome his brother the Green Knight, Sir Pertolepe; and his brother the Red Knight, Sir Perimones. And he said Beaumains should have homage and fealty of him and a hundred knights, to be always at his command, to go and ride wherever he should command them.

So they went to Sir Persant's pavilion and drank wine and ate spices.

The next morning when the damsel and Beaumains were taking their leave Sir Persant asked whither they were going.

"Sir," said the damsel, "this knight is going to the siege that besiegeth my sister in the Castle Perilous."

"Ah, ah," said Persant, "that is the Knight of the Red Lawns, who is the most dangerous knight that I know now living, and a man that is without mercy; and men say that he hath seven men's strength. God save you from that knight," he said to Beaumains; "for he doth great wrong to that lady; she is one of the fairest ladies of the world, and your damsel, I think, is her sister. Is not your name Linet?"

"Yes, sir, and my lady sister's name is Dame Liones."

"Now I will tell you," said Sir Persant, "this Red Knight of the Red Lawns hath lain well-nigh two years at siege; and many times he might have captured the lady, but he prolonged the time, hoping to have Sir Lancelot of the Lake to do battle with him, or Sir Tristram, or Sir Lamorak of Wales, or Sir Gawaine; and this is his reason for tarrying so long at the siege."

"Now, my lord Sir Persant of Inde," said Linet, "I require that you will make this gentleman knight before ever he fight with the Red Knight."

"I will, with all my heart," said Sir Persant, "if it please him to take the order of knighthood from so simple a man as I am."

"Sir," said Beaumains, "I thank you for your good will. I am well sped, for truly the noble knight Sir Lancelot made me knight."

"Ah," said Persant, "of a more renowned knight might ye not be made knight. For of all knights he may be called the chief of knighthood. All the world saith that knighthood is evenly divided between three knights—that is, Lancelot of the Lake, Sir Tristram of Lyonesse, and Sir Lamorak of Wales. There are many other noble knights, but there are none that pass these three. Therefore, God speed you well, for if you match the Red Knight, ye shall be called the fourth knight of the world."

"Sir," said Beaumains, "I would fain be of good fame and knighthood. I would have you know I come of good men, for my father was a noble man. And if you will keep it secret, and this damsel, I will tell you of what kin I am."

Then they both promised faithfully not to reveal who Beaumains was until he gave them leave.

"Truly, then," said he, "my name is Gareth of Orkney, and King Lot was my father, and my mother is King Arthur's sister; and Sir Gawaine is my brother, and Sir Agravaine, and Sir Gaheris, and I am the youngest of them all. And neither King Arthur nor Sir Gawaine know yet who I am."

THE RED KNIGHT OF THE RED LAWNS

Now the lady who was besieged in Castle Perilous heard that her sister Linet was approaching with a noble knight to rescue her. So she bade the dwarf who brought the tidings go to a hermitage near, and to take with him wine in two silver flagons, loaves of bread, fat venison, and dainty fowls.

"And a cup of gold I deliver thee that is rich and precious," she said; "and bear all this to my hermitage, and put it in the hermit's hands. Then go to my sister and greet her well, and commend me unto that gentle knight, and pray him to eat and to drink, and make him strong; and say to him I thank him for his courtesy and goodness for taking on him such labor for me that never did him bounty or courtesy. Also pray him that he be of good heart and good courage, for he shall meet with a full noble knight, but he has no bounty, courtesy, nor gentleness, for he thinks of nothing but murder, and that is the cause I cannot praise him nor love him."

So Beaumains and the damsel went to the hermitage, and there they drank the wine and ate the venison and the baked fowls. And when they had made a good repast the dwarf returned with his vessels to Castle Perilous. On his way there he met the Red Knight of the Red Lawns, who asked him whence he came and where he had been. Then the dwarf told him his lady's sister had come, and that she had brought with her a knight of King Arthur's Court.

"Then I account her trouble but lost," said the Red Knight, "for if she had brought with her Sir Lancelot, Sir Tristram, Sir Lamorak, or Sir Gawaine, I should think myself good enough for them all."

"It may well be," said the dwarf, "but this knight hath passed all the perilous passages, and hath slain the Black Knight and two others, and vanquished the Green Knight, and the Red Knight, and the Blue Knight, Sir Persant of Inde."

"Then he is one of the four I have just said."

"He is none of those, but he is a King's son."

"What is his name," said the Red Knight of the Red Lawns.

"That I will not tell you, but Sir Kay out of scorn called him 'Beaumains.'"

"I care not whatsoever knight he be, for I shall soon be quit of him. And if ever I am a match for him he shall have a shameful death, as many others have had."

"That were pity," said the dwarf, "and it is marvel that you should make such shameful war on noble knights."

That night Beaumains and the damsel stayed in the hermitage. On the morrow they took their horses and rode through a fair forest till they came to a plain, where they saw many pavilions and tents, and a splendid Castle, and there was much smoke and great noise. And when they came near the besiegers' camp, Beaumains as he rode espied upon great trees how there hung by the neck fully armed knights, their shields with their swords tied round their necks, and gilt spurs upon their heels; and thus hung there shamefully nearly forty knights richly armed.

Then Sir Beaumains' face darkened, and he said:

"What meaneth this?"

"Do not lose cheer because of this sight, fair sir," said the damsel, "for you must encourage yourself, or else you will be quite disgraced. For all these knights came hither to this siege to rescue my sister, Dame Liones; and when the Red Knight of the Red Lawns had overcome them he put them to this shameful death without mercy or pity. And in the same way he will serve you unless you quit you better."

"Now Christ defend me from such a villainous death and disgrace of arms," said Beaumains, "for rather than fare thus I would be slain like a man in plain battle."

"So it were better for you," said Linet. "Trust not there is any courtesy in the Red Knight; all his foes go to death or shameful murder. And that is pity, for he is a full likely man, well made of body, and a lord of great lands and possessions."

"Truly he may well be a good knight," said Beaumains, "but he useth shameful customs, and it is a marvel he endureth so long, and that the noble knights of my lord Arthur have not dealt with him."

Then they rode to the dikes, and saw they were double-diked, with full warlike walls, and there were lodged many great knights near the walls, and there was a great noise of minstrelsy. And the sea beat against one side of the walls, where there were many ships, and the shouting of mariners, "Hale and how! Pull ho!"

Fast by was a sycamore tree, and there hung a horn, the greatest that ever they had seen, made out of an elephant's tusk. The Knight of the Red Lawns had hung it there, so that if any errant knight came he must blow that horn, and then the Red Knight would arm himself and come to do battle.

"I pray you, sir, blow not the horn till it be high noon," said the damsel Linet; "for now it is about six o'clock, and at this time his might increases, so that, as men say, he hath seven men's strength."

"Ah, fie for shame, fair damsel, never more speak so to me," said Beaumains, "for if he were as good a knight as ever was, I shall never fail him in his greatest might, for either I will win honor honorably, or die knightly in the field."

Therewith Beaumains spurred his horse straight to the sycamore tree, and blew the horn so eagerly that all the camp and the Castle rang with it. Then there leaped knights out of their tents and pavilions, and those within the Castle looked over the walls, and out of the windows.

Then the Red Knight of the Red Lawns armed himself hastily, and two barons set his spurs upon his heels, and all was blood red, his armor, spear, and shield. And an earl buckled his helm upon his head, and then they brought him a red spear and a red steed, and so he rode into a little vale under the Castle, that all who were in the Castle and in the besieging camp might behold the battle.

THE LADY OF THE CASTLE PERILOUS

"Sir," said the damsel Linet to Sir Beaumains, "look you, be glad and gay, for here is your deadly enemy, and there at yonder window is my lady, my sister, Dame Liones."

"Where?" said Beaumains.

"Yonder," and the damsel pointed with her finger.

"She is the fairest lady that ever I looked on," said Beaumains, "and I ask no better for which to do battle. Truly she shall be my lady, and for her will I fight."

And he kept looking up to the window with a glad countenance.

And the Lady Liones made a deep curtsey to him, and they both waved their hands.

With that the Red Knight of the Red Lawns called to Beaumains:

"Leave thy looking, Sir Knight, and behold me, I counsel thee, for I warn thee well she is *my* lady, and for her I have done many strong battles."

"If thou hast so done," said Beaumains, "it seems to me it was but waste labor, for if she loveth none of thy fellowship, and thou to love one who loveth not thee is great folly. For if I understood she was not glad of my coming, I should think again before I did battle for her. But I know by the besieging of this Castle that she will have nothing to do with thee. Therefore, know well, thou Red Knight of the Red Lawns, I love her, and will rescue her, or else die."

"Sayest thou that?" said the Red Knight. "It seems to me thou oughtest to beware, by reason of yonder knights whom thou sawest hanging on those trees."

"Fie for shame," said Beaumains, "that ever thou shouldst do or say such evil, for in that thou shamest thyself and knighthood, and thou mayst be sure that no lady who knoweth thy wicked customs will love thee. And now thou thinkest that the sight of those hanged knights should frighten me? Nay, truly, not so. That shameful sight causes me to have courage and boldness against thee more than I would have had if thou wert a well-ruled knight."

"Make thee ready," said the Red Knight of the Red Lawns, "and talk no longer with me."

Then Beaumains bade Linet go to a safe distance, and both knights put spears in rest, and rushed together with all their might, so that they hurled each other to the ground, where both lay for a while sorely stunned. All those who were in the Castle and the camp thought their necks must be broken, and many said that the strange knight was a big man and a noble jouster, for before then they had never seen any warrior ever match the Red Knight of the Red Lawns;—and this they said both within the Castle and without.

Then Beaumains and the Red Knight left their horses and put their shields before them, and ran together like two fierce lions, and each gave the other such buffets on the helms that they both reeled back two strides,—then they recovered, and dealt such strokes that they hewed great pieces out of their armor and their shields.

Thus they fought till it was past noon, and after resting awhile, the battle went on again till evening, and none who beheld them could tell which was likely to win.

The Red Knight was a wily warrior, and his crafty fighting taught Beaumains to be wise, although he bought his experience dearly. For the Red Knight smote him on the hand, so that his sword fell out of it; and then he gave him yet another buffet on the helm, so that Beaumains fell grovelling to the earth, and the Red Knight fell over him, to hold him down.

Then cried the maiden Linet aloud:

"O, Sir Beaumains, where is thy courage? Alas, my lady sister beholdeth thee, and she sobbeth and weepeth, and maketh my heart heavy!"

When Sir Beaumains heard Linet speak thus, he started up with great might, and leaped to his sword, and gripping it in his hand, he rushed again on the Red Knight, and they fought a new battle together.

But Sir Beaumains doubled his strokes, and smiting the knight's sword out of his hand, felled him to the earth. And he unlaced his helm to slay him, but the Red Knight cried aloud:

"O, noble knight, I yield me to thy mercy!"

But Beaumains bethought him of the knights whom he had made to be hanged shamefully.

"I may not with honor save thy life," he said, "because of the shameful deaths thou hast caused full many good knights to die."

"Sir," said the Red Knight of the Red Lawns, "hold your hand, and ye shall know the cause why I put them to so shameful a death."

"Say on," said Beaumains.

"Sir, I once loved a lady, a fair damsel, and her brother was slain, and she said it was Sir Lancelot of the Lake, or else Sir Gawaine; and she prayed me that as I loved her heartily I would make her a promise by the faith of my knighthood, to labor daily in arms until I met with one of them, and all whom I overcame I should put to a villainous death. This is the cause why I have put all these knights to death, and thus ensured her vengeance against all King Arthur's knights. And now I will tell thee that every day my strength increaseth till noon, and all this time I have seven men's strength."

Then came many earls and barons and noble knights, beseeching Beaumains to save the Red Knight's life, and to make him a prisoner; they all fell upon their knees and prayed him to have mercy.

"Fair lords," said Beaumains, "be sure I am full loath to slay this knight, nevertheless he hath done passing ill and shamefully. But insomuch as all that he did was at a lady's request, I blame him the less, and so for your sake I will release him. He shall have his life upon this covenant—that he go within the Castle Perilous, and yield him there to the Lady Liones, and if she will forgive and acquit him, I will willingly, provided that he make her amends for all the trespass he hath done against her and her lands. Also," he continued to the knight, "when that is done, that ye go unto the Court of King Arthur, and there ask Sir Lancelot mercy, and Sir Gawaine, for the evil intention ye have had against them."

"All this will I do as ye command," said the Red Knight of the Red Lawns, "and certain assurance and sureties ye shall have."

So when the assurance was made, he paid his homage and fealty, and all those earls and barons with him.

Then the damsel Linet dressed his wounds, and those of Sir Beaumains. Ten days they sojourned in their tents, and the Red Knight made his lords and servants do all the pleasure they could to Sir Beaumains. And after praying pardon of the Lady Liones for all the wrongs he had done her, the Red Knight departed to the Court of King Arthur, and there openly put himself in the mercy of Sir Lancelot and Sir Gawaine.

Then Beaumains told Linet he desired to see her sister, his lady.

"I would fain ye saw her," she replied.

So Beaumains armed himself, and took his horse and his spear, and rode straight to Castle Perilous.

When he came to the gate he found many men armed, and the drawbridge pulled up, and the port closed. He marvelled why they would not suffer him to enter. Then he looked up to the window, and there he saw the fair Liones.

"Go thy way, Sir Beaumains," she cried, "for as yet thou shalt not have wholly my love, until the time that thou art called one of the number of the worthy knights. Therefore go labor honorably for twelve months, and then thou shalt hear new tidings."

"Alas, fair lady," said Beaumains, "I have not deserved that thou shouldst show me this strangeness. I thought I should have had right good cheer with you—I am well sure that I have bought your love with part of the best blood within my body."

"Fair courteous knight, be not displeased nor over hasty," said the Lady Liones. "Know well your great travail and good love shall not be lost, for I consider your great toil and labor, your bounty and your goodness, as I ought to do. Therefore go on your way, and look that you be of good comfort, for all shall be for your glory and for the best. By my faith, a twelvemonth will soon be done, and trust me, fair knight, I shall be true to you, and never forsake you, but to my death I shall love you, and none other."

Thus the noble knight, Sir Gareth, a King's son,—whom Kay had mocked at as his "Boy of the Kitchen,"—won for himself deathless honor, and his peerless bride. And he and Dame Liones, the Lady of the Castle Perilous, plighted troth to love each other and never to fail while their life lasted.

THE FOREST KNIGHT

THE BOYHOOD OF TRISTRAM

THERE was once a King called Meliodas, and he was lord of
the country of Lyonesse, and this King Meliodas was as
noble a knight as any living at that time. His wife was sister
of King Mark of Cornwall; she was called Elizabeth, and she
was both good and fair. At that time King Arthur reigned,
and he was King over the whole of England, Wales, and
Scotland, and of many other realms; there were many
princes of different countries, but they all held their lands
from King Arthur. For in Wales were two Kings, and in the
north many Kings; and in Cornwall and in the west were
two Kings; also in Ireland were two or three; and all were
under the obeisance of King Arthur.

125

The wife of King Meliodas was a gentle lady, and well she loved her husband, and he her again, and they were very happy together. But in that country lived a lady who was very angry, because long ago she had wanted to marry King Meliodas herself, although he had never cared for her. One day when the King rode out hunting, she made him by enchantment chase a hart by himself, till he came to an old Castle, and there he was at once taken prisoner by the wicked lady.

When the Queen Elizabeth missed her husband, she was nearly out of her mind with grief, and taking a gentle-woman with her, she ran out into the forest to seek the King.

And there in the midst of the cold and lonely forest, a little son was born, but death came to the poor mother. And when the Queen saw that there was no help but that she must needs die and depart out of this world, then she was very sad.

"When ye see my lord, King Meliodas, commend me to him," she said to her gentlewoman, "and tell him what I have endured here for his love, and how I must die here for his sake, with none to help me. And let him know that I am full sorry to depart out of this world from him, therefore pray him not to forget me. Now let me see my little child, for whom I have had all this sorrow." And when she saw him, she said in tender jesting, "Ah, my little son, thou hast killed thy mother, and therefore I suppose thou that art a murderer so young, thou art full likely to be a manly man in thine age." Then she charged the gentlewoman that she should beseech King Meliodas to call the child "Tristram,"—that is as much as to say "born in sorrow."

And with that, this Queen died.

The gentlewoman laid her under the shadow of a great tree, and wrapped the child as well as she could against the cold. At that moment up came the Barons, following after the Queen, and when they saw that she was dead, and imagined that the King also was destroyed, then certain of them would have slain the child, so that they might be lords of the country of Lyonesse.

But through the fair words of the gentlewoman the greater part of the Barons would not assent to it.

Then they carried the dead Queen home, and much dole was made for her.

In the meanwhile, Merlin the magician delivered King Meliodas out of prison on the morning after the death of his Queen, and when the King came home, most of the Barons were very joyful. But the sorrow that the King made for his Queen no tongue could tell.

The King had her richly interred, and afterwards had the child christened as his wife commanded before her death; and he had him called "Tristram,"—the child born in sorrow.

For seven years King Meliodas mourned for his wife, and all this time the young Tristram was nourished well.

But then it befell that King Meliodas wedded Duke Howell's daughter, of Brittany. By and by the new Queen had children of her own, and she grew jealous and angry that her children should not enjoy the country of Lyonesse, and because of this she planned to kill young Tristram. So she put some poison into a silver cup, in the chamber where Tristram and her children played together, intending that when Tristram was thirsty he should drink it. But it happened that the Queen's own little son as he was in the chamber espied the cup with poison, and being thirsty, and thinking it was good to drink, he swallowed it eagerly, and thereupon suddenly died.

When the Queen knew of her son's death, you may well imagine how grieved she was. But the King as yet understood nothing of her treason. Notwithstanding the death of her child, however, the Queen would not give up her wicked intention, but again she got some more poison and put it into a cup.

By chance King Meliodas found the wine in which the poison was, and being very thirsty, he took the cup to drink of it. Just as he was going to drink the Queen espied him, and running to him she pulled the cup suddenly away.

The King marvelled why she did so, and remembered how her son was suddenly slain with poison. Then he took her by the hand and said:

"Thou false traitress, thou shalt tell me what manner of drink this is, or else I will slay thee." And therewith he pulled out his sword.

"Ah, mercy, my lord," she cried, "and I will tell you all."

Then she told him how she would have slain Tristram, so that her own children should inherit the land.

"Well," said King Meliodas, "for this ye shall be tried by law."

By assent of the Barons the wicked Queen was condemned to be burned, and a great fire was made. But just as she was at the fire to undergo her sentence, young Tristram knelt before King Meliodas, and besought him to grant him a boon.

"I will, gladly," said the King.

"Then," said young Tristram, "give me the life of the Queen, my step-mother."

"That is not rightfully asked, for thou ought of right to

hate her, because she would have slain thee, if she could have had her will; and for thy sake there is most reason she should die."

"Sir," said Tristram, "as for that, I beseech you of your mercy that you will forgive it her; and as for my part, God forgive it her, as I do! And since it pleased your Highness to grant me my boon, for God's love I require you to keep your promise."

"Since that is so, I will let you have her life," said the King. "I give her to you. Go ye to the fire, and take her, and do with her what ye will."

So Tristram went to the fire, and by commandment of the King delivered the Queen from death.

For a long time King Meliodas would have nothing more to do with her, but at last by the good influence of young Tristram he was reconciled to his wife. The Queen never forgot how good Tristram had been to her, and ever afterwards she loved him dearly.

A KNIGHT ROYAL

When King Meliodas was reconciled with his Queen he sought out a tutor who was wise and learned, and under his care he sent young Tristram into France, to learn the language and customs, and deeds of arms. There with his tutor Gouvernail Tristram stayed more than seven years. When he could speak the language well, and had learned all he could learn in that country, he came home again to his father, King Meliodas. So Tristram learned to be a harper, passing all others—there was not found his equal in any country. Thus in his youth he applied himself to learn harping, and all instruments of music; and afterwards, as he grew in might and strength, he labored ever in hunting and hawking, more than any gentleman that was ever heard of. He set in order good measures concerning forest lore, and beasts of chase, and all manner of vermin, with all the terms used in hunting and hawking. Therefore the Book of the Chase, of Hunting and Hawking, is called the Book of Sir Tristram. Wherefore, all gentlemen that bear arms ought of right to honor Sir Tristram, for he taught such terms as gentlemen use to this day, so that all men of worth can distinguish a gentleman from a yeoman, and a yeoman from a peasant. For he that is gentle will draw to him those of gentle nature to follow the customs of noble men.

Tristram remained away till he was big and strong, and nineteen years old. When he returned home King Meliodas had great joy in his son, and so had the Queen his wife. For ever after in her life, because Tristram had saved her from the fire, she always loved him, and gave him many great gifts. And wherever he went, everyone loved him.

Soon after Tristram's return from France, it befell that King Anguish of Ireland sent to King Mark of Cornwall for his tribute, which Cornwall had paid many winters. But for seven years King Mark had not paid it, and now he and his Barons gave answer to the messenger from Ireland that they would pay nothing.

"Tell your lord," they said, "that if he wishes always to have tribute of Cornwall, let him send a trusty knight who will fight for his right, and we shall find another to defend our right."

With this answer the messenger departed back to Ireland.

King Anguish was very wroth at this answer, and he called to him Sir Marhaus, the good knight, who was nobly proved, and of the Round Table, and brother of the Queen of Ireland.

"Fair brother," he said, "I pray you go into Cornwall for my sake, and do battle for our tribute, which by right we ought to have; and whatsoever ye spend, ye shall have more than sufficient for your need."

Sir Marhaus consented gladly, and making ready in all haste, departed out of Ireland, and arrived in Cornwall, near to the Castle of Tintagel.

King Mark was very sorry when he heard that the good and noble knight Sir Marhaus had arrived to fight for Ireland, for he knew no knight who dared do battle with him, because at that time Sir Marhaus was one of the most famous and renowned knights of the world.

Thus Sir Marhaus abode in his ship off the coast, and every day he sent to King Mark to pay the tribute that was owing for seven years, or else to find a knight to fight with him. And the people of Cornwall made a proclamation in every place that whatever knight would fight to save the tribute of Cornwall, he would be rewarded so that he would fare the better for the rest of his life.

Some of the Barons counselled King Mark to send to the Court of King Arthur, to seek Sir Lancelot of the Lake, who was called at that time the most marvellous knight of all the world. But other barons counselled the King not to agree to this, saying it would be but labor in vain, because Sir Marhaus was a Knight of the Round Table, therefore any of the other knights would be loath to do battle with him, unless it were any knight at his own request, who would fight disguised and unknown. So the King and all his Barons agreed it was no use to seek any Knight of the Round Table.

Meanwhile rumor reached King Meliodas, how that Sir Marhaus abode fast by Tintagel, and how King Mark could find no manner of knight to fight for him.

When young Tristram heard of this he was wroth and sorely ashamed that no knight in Cornwall dared do battle with Sir Marhaus of Ireland. He accordingly went to his father, King Meliodas, and asked him counsel as to what King Mark was to do in order to keep his tribute, for it seemed a shame that Sir Marhaus should go away without any one doing battle with him.

"As for that," said Meliodas, "know well, my son Tristram, that Sir Marhaus is called one of the best knights of the world, and is a Knight of the Round Table; I know no knight in this country who is able to match him."

Then Tristram lamented that he was not yet made a knight, and he asked leave of his father to go to King Mark and be made knight by him. King Meliodas willingly agreed, so Tristram made ready, and rode into Cornwall. And when he came there he heard say no knight would fight with Sir Marhaus. Then he went to King Mark and said:

"Sir, if you will give me the order of knighthood, I will do battle with Sir Marhaus."

"What are ye?" said the King, "and whence are you come?"

"Sir, I come from King Meliodas, who wedded your sister; and that I am a gentleman you know well."

King Mark looked at Tristram and saw that he was but a young man in age, but he was passingly well-made and big.

"Fair sir," said the King, "what is your name, and where were you born?"

"Sir," he replied, "my name is Tristram, and in the country of Lyonesse was I born."

"Ye say well," said the King, "and if you will do this battle, I will make you knight."

"For that cause and no other I come to you," said Tristram; and then King Mark made him a knight.

Sir Marhaus heard that the King of Cornwall had found a young knight ready to do battle to the uttermost with him. "That is well," he said to the messenger, "but tell King Mark I will fight with no knight unless he be of royal blood, that is to say, either a king's son, or a queen's son, born of a prince or a princess."

King Mark sent for Sir Tristram and told him of Sir Marhaus's message.

"Let him know," said Tristram, "that I am come on father's

side and mother's side of blood as noble as he is. For, sir, now ye shall know that I am King Meliodas' son, born of your own sister, Lady Elizabeth, who died in the forest at my birth."

"Yea!" cried King Mark. "Fair nephew, ye are welcome to me."

Then in all haste King Mark ordered that Sir Tristram should be horsed and armed in the best manner that could be had for gold and silver, and he sent word to Sir Marhaus that a better born man than himself was ready to fight with him.

It was agreed that the battle should take place on an island near which lay Sir Marhaus's ship at anchor. So Sir Tristram was put into a vessel, both he and his horse, with everything that was needful for both of them; and when King Mark and his Barons saw how the young Sir Tristram departed to fight for the right of Cornwall, there was neither man nor woman of worship but lamented to see so young a knight thus jeopardy himself for their sake.

When Sir Tristram arrived on the island he looked to the further side, and there he saw six ships lying at anchor, and under the shadow of the ships on land appeared the noble knight, Sir Marhaus of Ireland. Then Sir Tristram bade his servant Gouvernail bring his horse to land, and help him to arm, and when he was in his saddle, well-apparelled, with his shield ready on his shoulder, he bade Gouvernail go back again to his vessel.

"Commend me to my uncle, King Mark," he said, "and pray him if I be slain in the battle to bury my body as seemeth best to him, and bid him know I will never yield me for cowardice. If I am slain and flee not, then have they lost no tribute for me; and if so be that I flee or yield as recreant, bid my uncle never bury me in Christian burial. And upon thy life come thou not nigh this island till thou see me overcome or slain, or else that I vanquish yonder knight."

So each departed from the other, weeping sorely.

When Sir Marhaus saw Sir Tristram, and how young he was, he was sorry for his daring, and he counselled him to return to his vessel; for the best knights in England and in the world had been matched with Sir Marhaus, and he had overthrown them.

But Sir Tristram replied that he could not forsake the quarrel, because for that he had been made knight. He was a King's son, born of a Queen, and he had promised his uncle, King Mark, to fight to the uttermost, and deliver Cornwall from the old tribute.

"And also know well, Sir Marhaus, this is the greatest reason that encourages me to fight with you, for thou art called one of the greatest knights in the world, and because of the fame thou hast, thou givest me courage to have ado with thee, for never yet was I proved with good knight. And since I took the order of knighthood today I am well pleased that I may have ado with so good a knight as thou art. And know, Sir Marhaus, that I seek to win worship because of thee, and if I am not yet proved, I trust I shall be honorably proved upon thy body, and deliver the country of Cornwall from all manner of tribute to Ireland for ever."

Sir Marhaus, having heard Tristram say what he would, spoke thus again:

"Fair knight, since it is the case that thou seekest to win worship because of me, I let thee know that thou wilt lose none, if thou canst stand me three strokes; for because of my noble deeds, proved and seen, King Arthur made me Knight of the Round Table."

Then they put their spears in rest and met so fiercely together that they smote each other down, horse and all. Sir Marhaus struck Tristram a great wound in the side with his spear, and then leaping clear of their horses, they pulled out their swords, and throwing their shields before them, lashed together as men that were wild and courageous. But when they had fought for a long time, Sir Tristram was fresher and stronger than Sir Marhaus, and with a mighty stroke he smote Sir Marhaus on the head with such a buffet that it went through his helm, and through the coif of steel, and through the brain-pan, and the sword stuck fast in the helm, so that Sir Tristram had to pull thrice at it before he could pull it out. And there Sir Marhaus fell down on his knees, the edge of Tristram's sword left in his brain-pan. Then suddenly he stumbled to his feet, and throwing his sword and his shield from him, he ran to his ships and fled his way; and Sir Tristram kept ever afterwards his shield and his sword.

So Sir Marhaus and his fellowship departed into Ireland. And as soon as he came to King Anguish, his brother-in-law, he had his wounds searched. And there in his head was found a piece of Sir Tristram's sword, and none of the surgeons were ever able to get it out, so Sir Marhaus died.

But after he was dead the Queen of Ireland, his sister, kept that piece of the sword always with her, for she determined to be revenged if ever she could.

LA BELLE ISEULT

Sɪʀ Tristram also had been sorely wounded, and after the fight with Sir Marhaus he sank down on a little hill, and could scarcely move. Then came Gouvernail with his vessel, and King Mark and his Barons came in procession, and when they got back to Cornwall the King took Tristram in his arms, and he and Sir Dinas the Steward carried Sir Tristram into the Castle of Tintagel. There he was tended in the best manner and laid in bed. And when King Mark saw his wounds he wept heartily, and so did all his Lords.

"God help me," said the King, "I would not for all my lands that my nephew died."

So Sir Tristram lay there a month and more, and ever he was likely to die of that stroke which Sir Marhaus smote him first with the spear. For the head of the spear was envenomed.

King Mark and all his Barons were passing heavy, for they thought that Sir Tristram would not recover of his wound. The King caused all sorts of doctors and surgeons to be sent for, both men and women, and there was not one who would promise that Tristram should live.

Then came a lady, who was a right wise lady, and she said plainly to Mark and Sir Tristram, and to all the Barons, that Tristram would never be whole unless he went into the same country where the venom came from, and in that country he would be helped, or not at all.

When King Mark heard this he ordered a fair vessel, well-provisioned, to be got ready for Sir Tristram, and the sick knight was put therein, and Gouvernail with him, and Sir Tristram took his harp with him. So they put out to sea, to sail to Ireland, and by good fortune they arrived in Ireland fast by a Castle where the King and Queen were; and on their arrival Tristram sat and harped in his bed a merry lay, such a one as they had never any of them heard in Ireland before that time.

When the King and Queen were told of the knight who was such a harper, the King immediately sent for him and had his wounds attended to, and then he asked him his name.

"I am of the country of Lyonesse, and my name is Tramtrist, and I was wounded in battle, as I fought for a lady's right," answered Tristram.

"Truly," said King Anguish, "ye shall have all the help in this land that ye may have. But I let you know that in Cornwall I had as great a loss as ever had a King, for there I lost the best knight of the world, his name was Marhaus,—a full noble knight, and a Knight of the Round Table," and he told Tristram how Marhaus had been slain.

Sir Tristram made a semblance of being sorry, but he knew better than the King how it was. He was afraid to reveal his real name, so he still pretended it was "Tramtrist."

King Anguish, as a great favor, made Tramtrist to be put into his daughter's ward and keeping, because she was a skilful surgeon. She discovered there was poison in the wound, and in the course of time she healed him. Then Tristram learned to have a great love for the beautiful Princess Iseult, for she was at that time the fairest maid and lady of the world. And there he taught her to harp, and she began to have a great fancy for him.

At that time there was a Saracen knight in the country who was much liked by the King and Queen. Sir Palamides was greatly attracted to the beautiful Iseult, and he offered her many gifts, for he loved her passing well. All this Sir Tristram saw, and full well he knew Sir Palamides for a noble knight and a mighty man. And he had a great grudge against Palamides, for Iseult told Tristram that the Saracen was willing to be christened for her sake. Thus there was great envy between Tristram and Sir Palamides.

Then it befell that King Anguish proclaimed a splendid joust and tournament for a lady who was called the "Lady of the Lawns," and she was a near cousin of the King's. Whatever man won her, should wed her after three days and have all her lands. This proclamation was made in England, Wales, Scotland, and also in France and in Brittany.

One day La Belle Iseult came to Sir Tristram, and told him of this tournament.

"Fair lady," he replied, "I am but a feeble knight, and lately I would have been dead, if it had not been for your good ladyship. Now, what would you that I should do in this matter? You know well that I cannot joust."

"Ah, Tramtrist," said La Belle Iseult, "why will you not take part in that tournament? I know well Sir Palamides will be there, to do what he can, and therefore, Tramtrist, I pray you be there also, or else Sir Palamides is likely to win the prize."

"Madam," said Tristram, "as for that, it may be so, for he is a proved knight, and I am but a young knight and lately made, and the first battle that I did, it misshaped me to be sorely wounded as ye see. But if I thought you would be my lady, I would go to that tournament, provided that you will keep my counsel, and let no creature know I shall joust, except yourself, and such as you will to keep your counsel. My poor person will I jeopard there for your sake, that peradventure Sir Palamides shall know when I come."

"Do your best," said La Belle Iseult, "and I will provide you with horse and armor."

"As you will, so be it," said Sir Tristram; "I will be at your command."

On the day of the joust came Sir Palamides with a black shield, and he overthrew many knights, so that all the people marvelled at him. All manner of knights dreaded Sir Palamides because of his prowess, and many called him "The Knight with the Black Shield." So that day Sir Palamides had great glory.

Then came King Anguish to Tristram, and asked him why he would not joust.

"Sir," said he, "I was but lately hurt, and as yet I dare not venture me," for he did not want the King to know he was going to fight.

On the morrow Sir Palamides made him ready to come into the field as he did the first day. And there he smote down the "King with a hundred Knights," and the King of Scotland.

La Belle Iseult had provided for Sir Tristram a white horse and white armor, and when he was well arrayed she let him out at a private postern, and so he rode forth into the field, as it had been a bright angel.

Sir Palamides quickly espied him, and therewith he feutered his spear at Tristram; and Tristram again at him; and there Sir Tristram smote down Palamides to the earth.

Then there was a great noise of people; some said Sir Palamides had a fall; some said the "Knight with the Black

Shield" had a fall. And you can well imagine La Belle Iseult was passing glad.

After that, no one would joust with Tristram, but all who were there kept out of his way.

Sir Palamides was sorely ashamed at receiving a fall, and, as privately as he could, he withdrew himself out of the field. Sir Tristram espied all this, and lightly he rode after Sir Palamides, and overtook him, and bade him turn, for he would test him better ere ever he departed. Then Palamides turned, and both lashed at each other with their swords. But at the first stroke Sir Tristram smote down Palamides, and gave him such a stroke upon the head that he fell to the earth. Then Tristram bade him yield him, and do his command, or else he would slay him.

When Sir Palamides saw his countenance he dreaded his buffets so much that he granted everything he asked.

Tristram made him promise that he would forsake following La Belle Iseult, and also for a twelvemonth and a day that he should bear no arms nor trappings of war.

"Promise me this, or here shalt thou die," said Tristram.

"Alas," said Palamides, "I am shamed forever!" But he swore to do as Tristram had commanded, and in his spite and anger, he cut off his armor and threw it away.

Tristram then rode privily to the postern, which La Belle Iseult kept for him, and there she made him good cheer, and thanked God for his success.

The King and Queen soon discovered that it was Tramtrist who smote down Palamides, and then he was made much more of than before.

THE BROKEN SWORD

Thus for a long time Sir Tristram stayed on in Ireland, and he was well cherished by the King and the Queen and La Belle Iseult. But one day it befell when he was out that the Queen and Iseult went into his room, and there, as it lay on the bed, the Queen beheld his sword. The Queen drew the sword from the scabbard, and looked at it, and both she and La Belle Iseult thought it a passing fair sword. But within a foot and a half from the point there was a great piece broken out of the edge.

When the Queen espied that gap in the sword, she remembered the piece of a sword that had been found in the brain-pan of Sir Marhaus, her brother.

"Alas!" she cried to her daughter, "this is the same traitor knight who slew my brother, thy uncle."

Iseult was sorely abashed to hear her say this, for she loved Sir Tristram passing well, and full well she knew the cruelty of her mother, the Queen.

The Queen went at once to her own chamber, and taking out from her coffer the piece of sword that had been found in Sir Marhaus's head, she ran with the piece of iron to the sword that lay on the bed. And when she put the missing piece against the blade, it was just as it might be when it was new broken.

The Queen was so angry at this discovery that she gripped the sword fiercely in her hand, and ran with all her might against Tristram where he sat unarmed.

She would have thrust him through, then and there, had not his squire, Sir Hebes, caught her in his arms, and pulled the sword from her. When she was prevented in her evil intention she ran to King Anguish, her husband.

"Oh, my lord," she cried, falling on her knees before him, "here have you in your house that traitor knight who slew my brother and your servant, the noble knight, Sir Marhaus."

"Who is that? And where is he?" said the King.

"Sir," she said, "it is Sir Tramtrist, the same knight whom my daughter healed."

"Alas," said the King, "I am much grieved for that, for he is as full noble knight as ever I saw in field. But I charge you, have no more to do with him, but let me deal with him."

Then the King went into the chamber to Sir Tramtrist, where he found him all ready armed to mount his horse.

"Nay, Tramtrist," said the King, "it will not avail thee to defy me. But this much I will do for my honor and thy love. Inasmuch as thou art within my Court it were no honor for me to slay thee. Therefore, I will give thee leave to depart from this Court in safety, on condition that thou wilt tell me who was thy father, and what is thy name, and if thou slew Sir Marhaus, the Queen's brother."

Then Tristram told King Anguish the whole story, and at the end the King said:

"Truly, I may not say but ye did as a knight should, and it was your part to do your best for your quarrel, and to increase your renown as a knight should. But I cannot keep you in this country in accordance with my honor, for I should displease my Barons, and my wife and her kin."

"Sir," said Tristram, "I thank you for the great kindness I have had here, and for the great goodness my lady your daughter hath shown me. It may so come to pass that you may win more by my life than by my death, for in parts of England haply I may do you service at some season, so that you will be glad you ever showed me honor. Moreover, I promise you, as I am a true knight, that in all places I shall be my lady your daughter's servant and knight, in right and in wrong, and I shall never fail her to do what a knight can do. Also, I beseech your good grace that I may take my leave of your daughter, and of all the barons and knights."

"Willingly," said King Anguish.

Then Sir Tristram went to La Belle Iseult, and took his leave of her.

"Oh, gentle knight," said Iseult, "full woe am I at thy departing, for I never saw man to whom I felt such good will." And therewith she wept heartily.

"Madam," said Sir Tristram, "now ye shall know that my name is Tristram of Lyonesse, son of King Meliodas, and of his Queen. And I promise you faithfully that I will be your knight all the days of my life."

"Great thanks!" said La Belle Iseult. "And I promise you that for the next seven years I will never marry but with your assent; and whom ye will that I shall marry, him will I have, if he will have me."

Then Sir Tristram gave her a ring, and she gave him another, and so he departed from her, leaving her in great sorrow.

Afterwards he went straight into the Court, among all the Barons, and there he took his leave of them, the greatest and the least, and spoke openly among them all.

"Fair lords, now thus it is, that I must depart. If there be any man here whom I have offended, or any man that is grieved with me, let him complain here before me, ere I depart, and I will amend it, as far as lies in my power. And if there be any who will proffer me wrong, or say of me evil behind my back, let him say it now or never, and here am I to make it good, man against man."

And they all stood silent; there was not one of them who would say a single word against him, though some of the knights were of the Queen's blood, and kin to Sir Marhaus.

HOW SIR TRISTRAM CAME TO CAMELOT

THUS Sir Tristram departed from Ireland, and sailed across the sea, and with a good wind he arrived at Tintagel in Cornwall. Tidings came to King Mark that Tristram had returned, and was healed of his wounds, at which King Mark rejoiced greatly, and all the Barons. Sir Tristram rode at once to his father, King Meliodas, and the King and the Queen, his stepmother, gave him the heartiest welcome, and bestowed on him much of their lands and treasure.

After spending some time at home, Tristram, by leave of his father, returned to the Court of King Mark, of Cornwall, where he lived in great joy for a long time, until at last there fell a great jealousy and unkindness between King Mark and himself, for they both loved the same lady.

One day when Tristram was on his way to visit her, he was suddenly attacked by three knights, and although he overcame them all and wounded them sorely, yet he was badly hurt himself in the conflict.

King Mark was one of these assailants, but he would not let it be known, and as for Sir Tristram he did not know it was the King with whom he had been fighting. The attendants of the King came to console Tristram as he lay sick in bed, for the crafty King pretended to be sorry for his nephew; thus passed many days and weeks, and apparently all was forgiven and forgotten.

But as long as King Mark lived he never afterwards loved Sir Tristram. Though there was fair speech, love there was none. The King cast always in his heart how he might destroy his nephew. Then it inwardly occurred to him to send Sir Tristram into Ireland to fetch La Belle Iseult. For Sir Tristram had so often praised her beauty and her goodness, that King Mark said he would wed her, wherefore he begged Sir Tristram to take his way into Ireland on an embassy. And all this was done with the intention of slaying Sir Tristram, for Mark knew of the enmity of King Anguish.

Nevertheless, since it was his uncle's pleasure, Sir Tristram would not refuse the errand because of any peril that might befall himself, but he made ready to go in the goodliest fashion that could be devised.

He took with him the noblest knights he could find at Court, and they were arrayed in the richest guise that was then the custom.

So Sir Tristram departed, and put to sea, with all his company. But as soon as they were out on the broad sea, a tempest took them, and drove them back to the coast of England, where they arrived fast by Camelot; and very glad they were to get safe to shore. When they were landed, Sir Tristram set up his pavilion on the lands of Camelot, and had his shield hung on the pavilion.

Now just at that time two knights, who were brothers, Sir Bleoberis and Sir Blamor de Ganis, nephews of Sir Lancelot of the Lake, summoned King Anguish of Ireland to come to Arthur's Court, on pain of forfeiture of King Arthur's good grace. And if the King of Ireland came not at the day assigned and set, he should lose his lands.

It happened that on the appointed day neither King Arthur nor Sir Lancelot could be there to give the judgment, for King Arthur was with Sir Lancelot at his Castle of Joyous Gard. King Arthur, therefore, assigned King Carados and the King of Scots to be at Camelot that day as judges, and while they were there, King Anguish of Ireland came to know his accusers.

Then Blamor de Ganis accused the King of Ireland of treason, that he had slain a cousin of the English knight's in his Court in Ireland, by treachery.

King Anguish was sorely abashed at this accusation. He had come at the summons of King Arthur, and before he reached Camelot he did not even know why he had been sent for. When he heard what Sir Blamor had to say, he understood full well there was no other remedy but to answer him knightly. For in those days it was the custom, if any man were accused of treason and murder, that he should fight body for body or else find another knight to fight for him. All kinds of murder in those days were called "treason."

King Anguish was passing heavy when he understood his accusation, for he knew that Sir Blamor de Ganis was a noble knight, and came of noble knights. The judges granted him a respite of three days to give his answer. So King Anguish departed to his lodging.

In the meantime, while Sir Tristram was in his pavilion at Camelot, Gouvernail his man came and told him how King Anguish of Ireland had come thither, and how he was put in great distress, and how he had been summoned and accused of murder.

"Truly," said Sir Tristram, "those are the best tidings that have come to me these seven years, for now shall the King of Ireland have need of my help, for I dare say there is no knight in this country, not of Arthur's Court, that dares to do battle with Sir Blamor de Ganis. To win the love of the King of Ireland, I will take the battle upon me, and therefore, Gouvernail, bring me, I charge thee, to the King."

Gouvernail accordingly went to King Anguish of Ireland, and saluted him fair. The King welcomed him, and asked him what he wished.

"Sir," said Gouvernail, "there is a knight near at hand who desireth to speak with you; he bade me say he would do you service."

"What knight is he?" asked the King.

"Sir," he said, "it is Sir Tristram of Lyonesse, who, for the good grace ye showed him in your lands, will reward you in this country."

"Come on quickly with me, fellow," said the King, "and lead me to Sir Tristram."

So King Anguish took a little riding horse, and only a few attendants, and came to Sir Tristram's pavilion.

When Sir Tristram saw the King, he ran towards him and would have held his stirrup. But the King leaped from his horse lightly, and they both embraced each other.

"My gracious lord," said Sir Tristram, "great thanks for all your goodness shown to me in your country. At that time I promised to do you service if ever it lay in my power."

"Gentle Knight," said the King, "now have I great need of you. Never had I so great need of any knight's help."

"How so, my good lord," asked Sir Tristram.

"I will tell you," said the King. "I am summoned from my country, and accused, because of the death of a knight who was kin to the good knight Sir Lancelot, wherefore Sir Blamor de Ganis, brother of Sir Bleoberis, hath challenged me to fight with him, or else to find a knight in my stead. I know well that those who come of King Ban's race, as Sir Lancelot and these others, are passing good knights, and as hard men to conquer in battle as any that I know now living."

"Sir," said Sir Tristram, "because of the honor you showed me in Ireland, and for my lady your daughter's sake, La Belle Iseult, I will take the battle for you on condition that ye shall grant me two things. One is that ye shall swear to me that ye are in the right, and that you never consented to the knight's death. Afterwards, when I have done this battle, if God give me grace that I succeed, ye shall give me a reward, what thing reasonable that I will ask of you."

"Truly," said the King, "ye shall have whatsoever ye shall ask."

"RATHER DEATH THAN DISHONOR"

"Now make your answer that your champion is ready," said Sir Tristram to King Anguish, "for I shall die in your quarrel rather than be recreant."

"I have no doubt of you," said the King, "even if you had to do battle with Sir Lancelot of the Lake."

"Sir," said Tristram, "as for Sir Lancelot, he is called the noblest knight of the world, and know ye well that the knights of his blood are noble men and fear shame; as for Sir Bleoberis, brother to Sir Blamor, I have done battle with him, therefore, on my head, it is no shame to call him a good knight."

"It is reported," said King Anguish, "that Sir Blamor is the hardier knight."

"Sir, as for that, let him be, he shall never be refused, were he the best knight that now beareth shield or spear."

King Anguish departed to King Carados and the Kings who were at that time as judges, and told them he had found his champion ready. Then, by command of the Kings, Sir Tristram and Sir Blamor de Ganis were sent for to hear the charge.

When they came before the judges, many Kings and knights beheld Sir Tristram, and there was much talking about him, because he had slain Sir Marhaus, the good knight, and because he overthrew in jousting the noble Saracen, Sir Palamides.

Having received their charge, the champions withdrew to make ready for battle.

Then said Sir Bleoberis to his brother, Sir Blamor:

"Dear brother, remember of what kin we are come, and what a man is Sir Lancelot of the Lake, neither further nor near than brother's children; there was never any of our kin that was ashamed in battle—but would rather suffer death, than to be ashamed!"

"Brother," said Blamor, "have no doubt of me, for I shall never shame any of my blood, howbeit I am sure that yonder knight is called a passing good knight, in his time one of the best in the world. Yet shall I never yield me, nor say the hateful word surrender. He may well happen to smite me down with his great might of chivalry, but he shall slay me rather than I shall yield me as recreant."

"God speed you well," said Bleoberis, "for ye shall find him the mightiest knight that ever ye had to do withal; I know him, for I have had to do with him."

"God speed me!" said Blamor de Ganis.

Therewith he took his horse at one end of the lists, and Sir Tristram at the other end, and so they levelled their spears and came together as though it were thunder, and there Sir Tristram, through great might, smote down Sir Blamor and his horse to the earth.

Sir Blamor leaped quickly clear of his horse, and pulling out his sword, threw his shield before him, and bade Sir Tristram alight.

"For though a horse has failed me, I trust the earth will not fail me," he cried.

Sir Tristram alighted, and there they lashed together strongly, smiting many heavy strokes, so that the Kings and knights marvelled greatly; for they fought as if they were mad, never knights were seen to fight more fiercely than they did; Sir Blamor was so hasty he would have no rest, and all men wondered that they had breath to stand on their feet. At the last, Sir Tristram smote Sir Blamor such a buffet upon the helm, that he fell down on his side, and Sir Tristram stood and looked at him.

When Sir Blamor could speak, he said thus:

"Sir Tristram of Lyonesse, I require thee as thou art a noble knight, and the best knight that ever I found, that thou wilt slay me outright,—I would not live to be made lord of all the earth, for I would rather die with honor than live with shame. Thou must needs slay me, Sir Tristram, or else thou wilt never win the field, for I will never say the hateful word. Therefore, if thou dare slay me, slay me, I require thee!"

When Sir Tristram heard him speak so knightly, he knew not what to do with him; he thought of both sides,—of what blood Sir Blamor came, and how for Sir Lancelot's sake he would be full loath to slay him; yet, on the other side, he could not choose but make Sir Blamor own himself vanquished, or else slay him.

For this was the law of the tournament.

Going to the Kings who were judges, Tristram knelt down before them, and besought them for their honor, and for King Arthur's, and Sir Lancelot's sake, that they would take this matter into their hands.

"For, my fair lords," said Sir Tristram, "it were shame and pity that this noble knight who lieth yonder should be slain, for ye hear well that shamed he will not be, and I pray to God that he be not shamed nor slain for me. And as for the King for whom I fight, I shall require him, as I am his true champion and true knight in this field, that he will have mercy on this good knight."

"Truly," said King Anguish to Sir Tristram, "I will for your sake be ruled as ye will have me; for I know you for my true knight. And therefore I will heartily pray the Kings who are here as judges to take the matter into their hands."

Then the Kings called Sir Bleoberis to them, and asked him his advice.

"My lords," said Bleoberis, "though my brother be beaten, and hath the worse through might of arms, I dare affirm that though Sir Tristram hath beaten his body, he hath not beaten his heart; and I thank God he is not shamed this day. And rather than he should be shamed, I require you let Sir Tristram slay him outright."

"It shall not be so," said the Kings, "for the adversary side, both the King of Ireland and his champion, have pity of Sir Blamor's knighthood."

"My lords," said Bleoberis, "whatever ye will, I agree to."

Then the Kings called the King of Ireland, and found him good and tractable. By the advice of all of them, Sir Tristram and Sir Bleoberis took up Sir Blamor, and the two brethren were reconciled with King Anguish, and kissed and made friends forever.

Sir Blamor and Sir Tristram also kissed together, and there they made their oaths that they would never, either of the two brethren, fight with Sir Tristram, and Sir Tristram swore a like oath that he would never fight with them.

And because of that gentle battle all the kindred of Sir Lancelot loved Sir Tristram forever.

Then King Anguish and Sir Tristram took their leave, and sailed into Ireland with great nobleness and joy. When they reached Ireland the King caused it to be known throughout all the land how and in what manner Sir Tristram had done for him, and the Queen and all who were there made the most of him that they could.

But the joy that La Belle Iseult made of Sir Tristram, no tongue could tell, for of all earthly men she loved him most.

THE MAGIC DRAUGHT

THEN upon a day King Anguish asked Sir Tristram why he did not ask his boon, for whatsoever he had promised him, he should have it without fail.

"Sir," said Tristram, "now is it time, this is all that I desire, that ye will give me La Belle Iseult, your daughter, not for myself, but for mine Uncle Mark that shall have her to wife, for so have I promised him."

"Alas," said the King, "I had rather than all the land I have, that ye would wed her yourself."

"Sir, if I did, then were I shamed for ever in this world, and false of my promise. Therefore," said Sir Tristram, "I pray you keep your promise that you gave me. For this is my desire,—that ye will give me La Belle Iseult to go with me to Cornwall, to be wedded to King Mark, my uncle."

"As for that," said King Anguish, "you shall have her with you to do what it pleases you,—that is to say, if you like to wed her yourself that is what would be dearest to me; and if you will give her to King Mark your uncle, you can do so, if you choose."

So La Belle Iseult was made ready to go with Sir Tristram, and Dame Bragwaine went with her for her chief gentlewoman, with many other ladies.

Before they left, the Queen, Iseult's mother, gave to Dame Bragwaine and to Gouvernail, Sir Tristram's attendant, a magic draught, and charged them that whatever day King Mark should wed, on that same day they should give him that draught, so that King Mark should drink to La Belle Iseult.

"And then," said the Queen, "I undertake that each shall love the other all the days of their life."

So the drink was given to Dame Bragwaine and to Gouvernail, and directly afterwards Sir Tristram put to sea with La Belle Iseult.

While they were in their cabin it so happened they were thirsty, and they saw a little flask of gold stand by them, and it seemed by the color and the taste that it was noble wine. Sir Tristram took the flask in his hand, saying:

"Madame Iseult, here is the best drink that ever ye drank, which Dame Bragwaine, your maiden, and Gouvernail, my servant, have kept for themselves."

Then they laughed and made good cheer, and each drank to the other in innocent mirth; and they thought that never drink that ever they drank was so sweet nor so good.

But after they had drunk that magic draught they each loved the other so well that never henceforth their love departed, either for weal or woe.

And this was how first happened the love between Sir Tristram and La Belle Iseult, the which love never departed all the days of their life.

So they sailed on, till by fortune they came near a Castle, where they stayed to repose themselves, thinking to have good harborage. But as soon as they were within the Castle they were taken prisoners, for the custom of the Castle was such, that whoever rode by it, and brought any lady, he must needs fight with the lord, whose name was Breunor. And if Breunor won the field, then he put to death the knight stranger and his lady, whoever they were. And if the strange knight won the field, then Sir Breunor and his lady should both die.

This had been the custom for many winters, and the name of the Castle, therefore, was called "Weeping Castle."

While Sir Tristram and Iseult were in prison, a knight and a lady came in to cheer them.

"I marvel," said Tristram, "what is the cause the lord of this Castle holdeth us in prison. It was never the custom of any honorable place, wherever I have been, that when a knight and a lady asked shelter, for the master to receive them, and afterwards to destroy those who were his guests."

The knight told Sir Tristram that it was an old custom of the Castle that when a knight went there, he must needs fight with the lord, and he who was the weaker must lose his head. And when that was done, if his lady that he brought with him was less beautiful than the wife of the lord, then she must lose her head; and if she were proved fairer than the lady, then the lady of the Castle must lose her head.

"Now," said Tristram, "this is a foul and shameful custom. But one advantage have I," he added. "I have a lady who is fair enough, fairer saw I never in all the days of my life, and I do not fear that for lack of beauty she will lose her head. And rather than I should lose my head, I will fight for it on a fair field. Wherefore, Sir Knight, I pray you tell your lord that I, with my lady, will be ready tomorrow for battle, if so be I may have my horse and mine armor."

"Sir," said the knight, "I undertake that your desire shall be sped right well. Take your rest, and look that ye be up betimes, for ye shall want nothing that is needful."

Early on the morrow the same knight came to Sir Tristram, and fetched him out of prison, with La Belle Iseult, and brought him his own horse and armor, and bade him make ready for the field, for all the people of that lordship were there ready to behold the judgment and the battle.

Then came Sir Breunor, lord of Weeping Castle, leading by the hand his lady, muffled, and he asked Sir Tristram where his lady was. For the one who was less fair must lose her head.

"Sir," said Tristram, "this is a foul and horrible custom, and rather than my lady should lose her head, I would more dearly lose my own."

"Nay, nay," said Sir Breunor, "the ladies shall be first shown together, and the one shall have her sentence."

"Nay, I will not so," said Sir Tristram, "for here is none who will give righteous judgment. But I doubt not my lady is fairer than thine, and that will I prove and make good with my hand. And whosoever he be that will say the contrary, I will prove it on his head."

And therewith Sir Tristram showed La Belle Iseult, and turned her thrice about, holding his naked sword in his hand. And Sir Breunor did the same with his lady. But when Breunor saw La Belle Iseult he thought he had never seen a lovelier lady. And all the people who were there present gave judgment that La Belle Iseult was the most beautiful.

"Truly," said Breunor, "thy lady is fairer than mine, and for that I repent sorely. Now must my lady be slain, and then I doubt not I shall slay thee, and marry thy lady."

"Thou shalt win her as dear as ever knight won lady," said Sir Tristram.

Then taking their horses, they rushed together like thunder, and thus they fought furiously, hurling here and there for nearly two hours, and both were sorely wounded. But at last Sir Tristram thrust Sir Breunor down grovelling, and killed him, and that was the end of the cruel and mischievous knight.

All the people who belonged to the Castle thereupon flocked to Tristram and did him homage and fealty, praying him that he should abide there a while, to do away with that evil custom. And to this Sir Tristram granted assent.

THE DRINKING-HORN OF MORGAN LE FAY

AFTER they had set things right in Weeping Castle, Sir Tristram and La Belle Iseult put to sea again, and came to Cornwall, where all the Barons met them. And King Mark and Iseult were richly wedded, with great splendor.

But because of the magic draught which they had drunk, Sir Tristram and La Belle Iseult ever loved each other dearly, and all the days of his life Sir Tristram was the true and faithful knight of Queen Iseult, and ever ready to do her loyal service.

Once when she was carried away by his old enemy, the Saracen knight, Palamides, and no one else at Mark's Court was strong enough to rescue her, Sir Tristram rode after them and set her free from the tower where she was imprisoned, and would have killed Sir Palamides if she had not begged him to spare his life. For he had never been christened, and she was loath that he should die a Saracen. For her sake, Tristram gave up fighting, and instead of being killed, Sir Palamides was commanded to leave the country, which he did, sorely against his will.

The pagan knight having departed in great heaviness, Tristram took the Queen, and brought her again to King Mark, and there was great joy at her homecoming. Who was cherished but Sir Tristram! Thus for a long while all was joy and pleasure.

But at King Mark's Court was a near cousin of Sir Tristram's, called Sir Andred, a spiteful and malicious man. He envied and hated Sir Tristram, because the latter was so gallant and noble a knight that every one loved him. Sir Andred dared not quarrel with him openly, but he lay always in watch to find him out in some secret fault, so that he might slander him to his uncle. King Mark was only too eager to believe any evil of Tristram, for he, too, was very jealous of his nephew, and had never forgotten the old grudge he bore him.

So it happened on a day Sir Tristram talked with Queen Iseult, and Sir Andred espied them, and hoping to make mischief, went and told the King. King Mark came in a great rage, with his sword in his hand, and called him "false traitor," and would have struck him. But Tristram, being very near, ran under the sword, and seized it from the King's hand.

"Where are my knights and my men?" cried the King. "I charge you, slay this traitor!"

But none of them would move.

Sir Tristram, seeing that not one would be against him, made as though he would strike the King, whereupon Mark fled. Then Tristram went his way, and armed himself, and taking his horse and his man, rode into the forest.

King Mark sent many knights after him, but Sir Tristram killed two and wounded many more, and not one of them could overcome him. Then King Mark called his council, and asked advice of his Barons, what it was best to do with Sir Tristram.

"Sir," said the Barons, and especially Sir Dinas, the Steward, "we counsel you to send for Sir Tristram, for we would have you know that many men will side with Sir Tristram, if he is hard pressed. Ye shall understand, sir, that Tristram is called peerless and matchless of any Christian knight, and of his might and hardihood we know none so good a knight, unless it be Sir Lancelot of the Lake. If he depart from your Court, and go to King Arthur's Court, mark ye well, he will find such friends there that he will care nothing for your malice. Therefore, sir, we counsel you to take him into your favor."

"I am willing that he be sent for, that we may be friends," said the King.

Then the Barons sent for Sir Tristram, under a safe conduct. When the knight came back to Court he was made welcome; nothing was said about what had happened, and there were sport and amusement; the King and the Queen went out hunting, and Tristram went with them.

About this time Morgan le Fay, the wicked sister of King Arthur, sent a present to her brother. It was a beautiful drinking-horn, mounted with gold, and it was supposed to have some magic power, so that no lady or gentlewoman could drink of it unless she truly loved her husband; if she did not love him, then all the liquid would be spilled. Because Morgan le Fay hated Queen Guinevere, she had sent this horn to King Arthur, hoping to work some mischief by her evil spells.

The messenger who carried the horn happened to meet a knight of King Mark's, called Sir Lamorak, whom Sir Tristram had just defeated in some joust, and who was longing to be revenged. Knowing King Mark's hatred of Sir Tristram, and his jealousy because everyone loved him, Sir Lamorak thought it would be a good plan to seize the horn and send it to King Mark, and make him try the trick on Queen Iseult. He threatened to kill the messenger unless the latter obeyed his command, and the enchanted horn was therefore presented to King Mark.

The King made Queen Iseult drink out of it, and a hundred ladies of the Court, and only four among them all could drink without spilling. Then in his rage the cruel King swore an oath that Iseult and all the other ladies should be burned to death.

But the Barons gathered themselves together and said plainly they would not have those ladies burned because of a horn made by sorcery, which came from as wicked an enchantress as any then living. For that horn never did any good, but always caused strife and debate, and all her life Morgan le Fay had been an enemy to all true and loving people. And many knights declared that if ever they met with Morgan le Fay they would show her short courtesy.

Sir Tristram also was very angry that Sir Lamorak had sent the horn to King Mark, for he knew well it was meant to work him harm.

ISEULT OF BRITTANY

Sir Andred, in the meanwhile, was always on the watch to see how he could trap Sir Tristram, and at last his opportunity came. One day, with twelve knights, he fell on him secretly and suddenly, and bound him hand and foot. Then by assent of King Mark, Tristram was taken to a little chapel on the sea-rocks, there to receive judgment, and he was led bound between forty knights.

When he saw there was no escape, but that he must needs die, then he said:

"Fair lords, remember what I have done for the country of Cornwall, and what jeopardy I have been in for the weal of you all. For at the time I fought for the tribute of Cornwall against Sir Marhaus, when ye all refused to take the battle, I was promised to be better rewarded. Therefore as ye be good, gentle knights, see me not thus shamefully die, for it is a shame to all knighthood thus to treat me. For I dare say that I never yet met with any knight, but was as good as he, or better."

"Fie upon thee," said Sir Andred, "false traitor as thou art with thy vaunting! For all thy boast thou shalt die this day."

"O Andred, Andred," said Sir Tristram, "thou shouldst be my kinsman, and now thou art to me full unfriendly! But if there were no more but thou and I, thou wouldst not put me to death."

"No!" said Sir Andred, and therewith he drew his sword and would have slain him.

When Sir Tristram saw this threatening movement, he looked at both his hands, which were fast bound to two knights, and suddenly he pulled them to him, and wrenched them free; then he leaped to his cousin Andred, and wrested his sword out of his hand, and smote him to the earth; and thus he fought until he had killed ten knights. Then he got inside the chapel, and held it bravely.

But the outcry was great, and numbers of people—more than a hundred—flocked quickly to Sir Andred. When Sir Tristram saw the people draw near, he remembered he was without armor, and making fast the door of the chapel, he broke the bars of a window, and so leaped out, and fell upon the crags into the sea. And at that time neither Sir Andred nor any of his fellows could get at him.

In the meanwhile, Gouvernail and two of Sir Tristram's men sought their master. When they heard he had escaped, they were very glad, and on the rocks they found him, and pulled him up.

Tristram asked where La Belle Iseult was, for he thought Sir Andred's people had carried her away. But Gouvernail replied that she had been shut up in a horrible little hut, kept apart for the use of sick folk, ill of dangerous diseases.

"Alas!" said Sir Tristram, "this is a foul place for such a fair lady, and if I may, she shall not be long there," and so he went with his men, and fetched away Queen Iseult, and brought her into a forest to a fair Manor, where she abode, for she was afraid to go back to her husband, King Mark.

One day Sir Tristram went into the forest for a little sport, and it so happened that there he fell asleep. And a certain man, whose brother Tristram had killed some time before, came that way, and finding him asleep, shot him through the shoulder with an arrow.

Meanwhile it had been told King Mark how Sir Tristram had taken Queen Iseult out of the hut, and placed her in the Manor, and as soon as the King heard of it, he came thither with many knights to slay Sir Tristram. But he arrived when Tristram was absent in the forest, so he took La Belle Iseult home with him, and afterwards kept her so closely shut up that by no means in her power could she send word to Tristram, nor he to her.

When Sir Tristram returned from the forest to the old Manor he found the track of many horses, and thereby he knew his lady was gone. Then he was very sorrowful, and for a long time he endured great pain, for the arrow with which he had been hurt was envenomed.

At last, through some lady who was a cousin to Dame Bragwaine, Queen Iseult sent a message to Sir Tristram. She told him he would by no means be cured in Cornwall, for she was not able to help him. Therefore she bade him haste into Brittany, to King Howell, and there he would find the King's daughter, Iseult of the White Hands, and she would help him.

So Sir Tristram and Gouvernail took ship, and sailed to Brittany. King Howell was very glad when he knew it was Sir Tristram of Lyonesse who had come. Tristram said he had come to his country to have help from his daughter, for it had been told him that no one else could cure him.

And there, in a little while, Iseult of Brittany healed Sir Tristram of his hurt.

Now it happened at that time in Brittany there was an earl called Grip, who made great war on King Howell, and put him to the worse, and besieged him. And once when Sir

Kehydius, the King's son, issued out, he was sorely wounded, nearly to death.

Gouvernail thereupon went to the King, and said:

"Sir, I counsel you to desire my lord, Sir Tristram, to help you in your need."

"I will do as you counsel," said the King. So he went to Sir Tristram, and prayed him to help him in his wars, because his son Kehydius could not go into the field.

"Sir," said Tristram, "I will go to the field, and do what I can."

He sallied forth from the town, with all the company he could collect, and did such deeds that all Brittany spoke of him. And at last, by great force and might, he slew with his own hands Earl Grip, and many of his knights.

On his return to the town Sir Tristram was received in high honor, with a procession. King Howell embraced him, and said:

"Sir Tristram, all my kingdom I will resign to thee."

"God forbid," said Sir Tristram, "for I am beholden to do what I can for you, for your daughter's sake."

Then King Howell and his son Kehydius thought how good it would be if Sir Tristram wedded Iseult of the White Hands; a great liking grew up between Tristram and Iseult, for that lady was both good and fair, and a woman of noble blood and fame. And because Sir Tristram had such cheer and riches, and all other pleasantness, he almost for a time forgot La Belle Iseult, who had loved him long ago.

So he agreed to wed Iseult of Brittany, and at last they were wedded, and the marriage was held with great solemnity and splendor.

THE FOREST OF STRANGE ADVENTURES

When Queen Iseult heard that Sir Tristram was wedded to Iseult of Brittany, she sent him letters by her maiden Bragwaine, saying that if it pleased Sir Tristram to go to her Court and take with him Iseult of the White Hands, they should be treated right well.

Sir Tristram did not think it well to take his wife to Cornwall, for he knew not what might happen, through the enmity of King Mark. But he called his brother-in-law, Sir Kehydius, and asked him whether he would go with him. He answered that he was ready at all times. So a little vessel was quietly prepared, and therein they went—Sir Tristram, Kehydius, Dame Bragwaine and Gouvernail, Sir Tristram's squire.

When they were at sea a contrary wind took them on to the coast of North Wales, near the Castle Perilous. Then Tristram said to Dame Bragwaine, "Wait here for me ten days, and Gouvernail, my squire, shall stay with you. And if so be I come not by the end of that time, take the nearest way into Cornwall, for in this forest are many strange adventures, I have heard say, and some of them I intend to prove before I depart. And when I can, I will hie after you."

Sir Tristram and Sir Kehydius took their horses, and left their companions, and rode through the forest a mile and more. And there they came across a knight-errant, with whom they jousted, but at the first encounter Sir Kehydius got a fall, and was sorely wounded. So Sir Tristram and the other knight, Sir Lamorak of Wales, set him on a shield, and bore him betwixt them to the lodge of a forester, to whom they gave charge that Sir Kehydius was to be well kept. After three days the other two knights took their horses, and at the cross roads they parted.

As Sir Tristram rode on his way alone, he chanced to meet Sir Kay, the Steward, that same knight who had so spitefully treated Sir Gareth, son of King Lot of Orkney, and nicknamed him "the Boy of the Kitchen." Sir Kay asked Sir Tristram of what country he was; the latter answered that he was of the country of Cornwall.

"It may well be," said Sir Kay, sneeringly, "for I never yet heard that ever good knight came out of Cornwall."

"That is evil spoken," said Sir Tristram, "but I require you to tell me your name."

"Sir, my name is Sir Kay, the Steward."

"Is that your name?" said Sir Tristram, "now wit ye well that ye are called the shamefullest knight of your tongue now living; howbeit, ye are called a good knight, but unfortunate, and most spiteful with your tongue."

Thus they rode together till they came to a bridge, and here stood a knight, who would not let them pass till one of them jousted with him. So the knight jousted with Sir Kay, and there he gave him a fall; the knight's name was Sir Tor, half-brother to Sir Lamorak, and they were the sons of Pellinore, with whom King Arthur had once fought.

Then Sir Tristram and Sir Kay rode to their lodging, where they found another knight, named Sir Brandiles, and Sir Tor came thither soon after.

As the four knights sat at supper three of them spoke all shame of Cornish knights. Tristram heard what they said, and he spoke but little, but he thought the more, and he did not at that time reveal his name.

On the morrow he took his horse, and went with them. On the way Sir Brandiles proffered to joust with him, and Sir Tristram smote him down, horse and all, to the earth. Then Sir Tor encountered with Sir Tristram, and Sir Tristram smote him, also, down. Then he rode on alone; Sir Kay followed him, but Tristram would not have his company.

"I would fain know what is that knight's name," said Sir Brandiles, coming up to Sir Kay.

"Come on with me," said Sir Kay, "and we will pray him tell us his name."

They rode together till they came near Tristram, and saw where he sat by a well, and had put off his helm, to drink at the well. When he saw them come he laced on his helm, and took his horse and proffered them to joust.

"Nay," said Sir Brandiles, "we jousted late enough with you, we come not with that intent. But we come to require you of knighthood to tell us your name."

"My fair knights, since that is your desire, and to please you, ye shall know that my name is Tristram of Lyonesse, nephew to King Mark of Cornwall."

"In good time, and ye are well found!" said Sir Brandiles. "Wit ye well that we are right glad we have found you, and we are of a fellowship that would be right glad of your company. For ye are the knight in the world whom the fellowship of the Round Table most desireth."

"I thank them for their great goodness," said Sir Tristram, "but as yet I feel I am unable to be of their fellowship. For I was never of such deeds of worthiness to be in the company of such a fellowship."

"Ah," said Sir Kay, "if ye be Sir Tristram of Lyonesse, ye are the man now called most of prowess, except Sir Lancelot of the Lake. For that man is not alive, either Christian or heathen, who can find such another knight, to speak of his prowess, and his hands, and his truth withal. For never yet could anyone say of him dishonor, and make it good."

Thus they talked a great while, and then they departed one from another, such ways as seemed best to them.

Now about this time a wicked enchantress called the Lady Anna, by fair words and artful cunning enticed King Arthur to ride with her into the Forest Perilous; she was a great sorceress, and had loved King Arthur many days, and therefore she came into that country. When King Arthur had gone with her, and his knights missed him, many of them followed after him, such as Sir Lancelot, Brandiles and others.

The sorceress took King Arthur to her tower, and hoped to win his love, but the King remembered his own lady, Queen Guinevere, and would not love the enchantress for any craft she could do. Then every day she made him ride into the forest with his own knights, with the intent of having him slain. For when this Lady Anna could not have her will she labored by false means to have King Arthur destroyed and slain.

But the Lady of the Lake,—whose name was Vivien—who was always friendly to King Arthur, discovered by her subtle craft that the King was in great danger, and therefore she came into the Forest Perilous, to seek after Sir Lancelot or Sir Tristram, to help King Arthur. For on that same day the Lady of the Lake knew well King Arthur would be slain, unless she had help of one of these two knights.

Thus she rode up and down until she met with Sir Tristram, and as soon as she saw him, she knew him.

"Oh, my lord Sir Tristram," she said, "well are ye met, and blessed be the time I have met with you! For this same day and within these two hours shall be done the foulest deed that ever was done in this land."

"Oh, fair damsel," said Sir Tristram, "may I amend it?"

"Come on with me," she said, "and that with all the haste ye may, for ye shall see the most worshipful knight of the world hard bested."

Then said Sir Tristram, "I am ready to help such a noble man."

"He is neither better nor worse than the noble King Arthur himself," said the Lady of the Lake.

"God forbid that ever he should be in such distress," said Sir Tristram.

They rode together a great pace, until they came to a little turret or castle, and underneath that castle they saw a knight standing on foot, fighting with two knights. Sir Tristram watched them, and at last saw the two knights smite down the one knight, and one of them unlace his helm to slay him. And the Lady Anna got King Arthur's sword in her hand, to strike off his head.

Therewith Sir Tristram rushed forward with all his might, crying, "Traitress, traitress, leave that!" and he quickly smote one knight after the other, so that both fell dead.

In the meanwhile the Lady of the Lake cried to King Arthur, "Let not that false lady escape!" and King Arthur overtook the wicked sorceress, and with the same sword she held in her hand he smote off her head.

Sir Tristram set King Arthur on horseback, and rode forth

173

with him, but he charged the Lady of the Lake not to reveal his name at that time. When the King was mounted he thanked Sir Tristram heartily, and desired to know his name, but Tristram would not tell him, except that he was a poor knight adventurous. And so he bore the King company until he met with some of his own knights.

Within a mile they met with Sir Ector de Maris, who did not know either King Arthur or Sir Tristram, and desired to joust with one of them. Sir Tristram accepted his offer, and at once smote him from his horse. Having done so, he came again to the King, and said:

"My lord, yonder is one of your knights, he can bear you fellowship, and another day, by that deed which I have done for you, I trust ye will understand that I would do you service."

"Alas," said King Arthur, "let me know whom you are."

"Not at this time," said Sir Tristram.

So he departed, and left King Arthur and Sir Ector together.

THE WILD MAN OF THE WOODS

On a day appointed, Sir Tristram went back to the forester's
lodge where Sir Kehydius had been left to get well of his
wounds, and they rode to the ship where Dame Bragwaine
and Gouvernail were waiting for them, and so they sailed
all together to Cornwall.

Queen Iseult rejoiced more than tongue can tell to see Sir
Tristram again, but Tristram could not remain in the Castle
of Tintagel, for King Mark still hated him, and would have
slain him if he could. So taking his horse and armor he rode
away into the forest, and there for many days he dwelt in
loneliness and bitter sorrow. No one knew what had become
of him. A damsel from the Court went out to seek him, but
nothing she could say or do would give him any comfort,
nor would he eat any meat or drink when she brought it him.
Then in his wanderings it happened that he came near the
same Castle where he and Sir Palamides did battle when La
Belle Iseult parted them. And the damsel went to the lady
of the Castle, and told her of the misadventure of Sir Tristram.

"Alas," said the lady, "where is my lord Sir Tristram?"

"Right here by your Castle," said the damsel.

"In good time is he so nigh me," said the lady, "he shall

have meat and drink of the best, and a harp I have of his whereon he taught me,—for of goodly harping he beareth the prize in the world."

So this lady and the damsel brought Tristram meat and drink, but he ate little thereof. He put his horse from him, and unlaced his armor, and then he wandered away into the wildest parts of the wood; sometimes he burst down trees and boughs, and at other times when he found the harp which the lady sent him, then he would play thereon, and weep. And sometimes when Sir Tristram was in the wood, and the lady of the Castle knew not where he was, she would sit down and play upon the harp; then would Sir Tristram come and hearken to it, and sometimes would harp himself.

Thus he endured for several months, but in the end he ran away and she knew not what became of him.

Now came a sad time for poor Sir Tristram. He sorrowed so deeply and was so long in the lonely forest that his mind quite went, and he lost all memory of knightly things. His clothes fell off in tatters, and he waxed lean and poor of flesh and so he fell into the company of herdsmen and shepherds, and daily they would give him of their meat and drink, and they clipped him with shears, and treated him like a fool.

But although he had lost his mind, he was still brave in spirit, and strong in body. Once when his friends, the herdsmen were threatened by Sir Dagonet, King Arthur's fool and two squires, Sir Tristram ran to their help, overthrew Dagonet, killed one of the squires, and drove the other away.

In the meanwhile, his wicked cousin Sir Andred caused it to be noised abroad that Sir Tristram was dead. He got some lady to tell a false tale at King Mark's Court, that she was with Sir Tristram when he died, and that she had buried him by a well, and that before he died he besought King Mark to make his cousin Sir Andred King of the country of Lyonesse, of which Sir Tristram was lord. All this Sir Andred did because he wanted to have Sir Tristram's lands.

King Mark wept and pretended to make great lamentation when he heard that Sir Tristram was dead. But when these tidings reached Queen Iseult she made such sorrow that she was almost out of her mind; she fell ill of grief, and lay for a long time sick nearly to the point of death.

Now in that country there was a giant called Tauleas. From fear of Tristram, for more than seven years he never dared go much at large, but for the most part kept in a strong Castle of his own. But when Tauleas heard from the report at Mark's Court that Tristram was dead, then he went out daily. So it happened one morning he came across the herdsmen, wandering and lingering round a well in the forest, and sat himself down to rest among them.

While he was there, up came a knight of Cornwall, called Sir Dinant, leading with him a lady. The giant seeing him, went from the herdsmen, and hid himself under a tree; and the knight came to the well, and there he alighted to rest.

As soon as he was away from his horse, the giant Tauleas came betwixt this knight and his horse, and took the horse and leaped on it. Then he rode at Sir Dinant, and seizing him by the collar, pulled him up before him, and would have stricken off his head.

"Help yonder knight!" cried the herdsmen to Sir Tristram.

"Help him yourselves!" said Tristram.

"We dare not," said the herdsmen.

Then Tristram saw the sword of the knight where it lay on the ground, and he ran and took it up, and struck off the head of the giant, and so went his way back to the herdsmen again.

Sir Dinant on his return to Court told King Mark of the adventure that had betided him in the forest, and how a wild man had rescued him from the grim giant Tauleas.

"Where had you this adventure?" asked King Mark.

"At the fair fountain in your forest where many adventurous knights meet," said Sir Dinant, "and there is the mad-man."

"Well," said King Mark, "I will see that wild man."

So within a day or two King Mark commanded his knights and his huntsmen that they should be ready the next morning to hunt, and on the morrow he went into the forest. And when he came to the well he found there, lying asleep, a comely man, with a sword by him. The King commanded his knights to take him up gently, and bring him to the Castle of Tintagel, which they did. And there they bathed him and washed him, and gave him hot food, so that presently Sir Tristram quite recovered his lost memory.

But all this while there was not a creature who knew Sir Tristram, nor what man he was.

It fell on a day that the Queen, La Belle Iseult, heard of the wild man of the forest, and how the King had brought him home to the Court. Then Queen Iseult called Dame Bragwaine to her, and said, "Come with me, for I will go see this man whom my lord brought from the forest." So they passed forth, and asked where was the sick man. A squire told the Queen that he was in the garden taking his rest, reposing in the sun.

When the Queen looked at Sir Tristram, she did not remember him, but still she kept saying to Bragwaine, "It seems I must have seen him before now in many places."

But as soon as Sir Tristram saw Iseult, he knew her well enough, and he turned away his face and wept.

Now the Queen had always a little dog with her, that Sir Tristram gave her the first time she ever came into Cornwall, and never would the little dog leave her unless Sir Tristram himself were also near.

As soon as this little dog came near Tristram, she leaped upon him, and licked his cheeks and his ears, and whined and jumped about all over him.

"Ah, my lady!" said Dame Bragwaine to La Belle Iseult.

"Alas, alas!" cried the Queen, "I see its mine own lord Sir Tristram!" and thereupon she fell down in a swoon, and lay senseless for a long time, for she was startled to see Tristram alive, after so long believing him to be dead. By and by, when she could speak, she said, "My lord Sir Tristram, blessed be God ye have your life! Now I am sure ye will be discovered by means of this little dog, for she will never leave you; and also I am sure that as soon as my lord King Mark knows you, he will banish you out of the country of Cornwall, or else he will destroy you. Therefore grant King Mark his will, and go you to the Court of King Arthur, for there ye are beloved. And whenever I can, I shall send unto you, and when you like, you can come to see me, and at all times early and late I will be at your command to live as poor a life as ever did Queen or lady."

"Oh, madam," cried Sir Tristram, his heart torn with grief and pity, "leave me, I pray, for much anger and danger have I endured for your sake."

Then the Queen departed, but the little dog would not leave him.

"FOR LOVE OF SIR LANCELOT!"

Soon after Queen Iseult had departed, came King Mark, and the little dog set upon him, and bayed at them all. "Sir, this is Sir Tristram, I see by the dog," spoke Sir Andred.

"Nay," said the King, "I cannot suppose that," and he asked Tristram to tell him faithfully who he was, and what was his name.

"Truly," said the knight, "my name is Sir Tristram of Lyonesse; now do to me what you please."

"Ah," said King Mark, "I am sorry for your recovery." And he had his Barons summoned, to judge him to death.

Many of the Barons would not consent to that, so by the advice of them all, Sir Tristram was banished out of the country for ten years. Thus he was made to depart out of Cornwall, and many Barons went with him to his ship, of whom some were his friends, and some his foes.

In the meanwhile, arrived a knight of King Arthur's, whose name was Dinadan, and his coming was to seek after Sir Tristram. Then they showed him where Tristram was armed at all points, ready to start for the ship.

"Now, fair knight," said Dinadan, "before you pass from this Court, I challenge you to joust with me."

"With a good will," said Tristram, "if these lords will give me leave."

The Barons granted it, and so the knights charged at each other, and there Sir Tristram gave Sir Dinadan a fall. Then Dinadan begged leave to go with him.

"Ye shall be right welcome," said Tristram. So they took their horses, and rode to their ships together.

When Sir Tristram was on his ship, he turned and spoke to the Barons who had gone with him.

"Greet well King Mark and all mine enemies," he said, "and tell them I will come again when I can. And well am I rewarded for the fighting with Sir Marhaus, and delivering all this country from serfdom; and well am I rewarded for the fetching of La Belle Iseult out of Ireland, and the danger that I was in, first and last, and on the way coming home, the peril I had to save Queen Iseult from Weeping Castle! And well am I rewarded when I fought with Sir Blamor de Ganis for King Anguish, father of La Belle Iseult. And well am I rewarded when I smote down the good knight Sir Lamorak of Wales at King Mark's request! And well am I rewarded when I fought with the King of the Hundred Knights, and the King of North Wales, both of whom would have put his land in serfdom, and by me they were put to rebuke. And well am I rewarded for the slaying of Tauleas, the mighty giant! And many more deeds have I done for him, and now have I my recompense! —Tell King Mark that many noble knights of the Round Table have spared the Barons of this country for my sake. Also am I not well rewarded when I fought with the good knight Sir Palamides, and rescued Queen Iseult from him? And at that time King Mark said before all his Barons I should have been better rewarded."

And forthwith Sir Tristram set out to sea.

At the next landing, near the sea, Sir Tristram and Sir

Dinadan met with two knights, Sir Ector de Maris and Sir Bors de Ganis, who challenged them to a trial of strength. Sir Ector jousted with Sir Dinadan and smote him and his horse down, and Sir Tristram would have jousted with Sir Bors, but Sir Bors said he would joust with no Cornish knights, for they are not called men of honor.

Just then up came two more knights, one of whom, Sir Bleoberis, proffered to joust with Sir Tristram, who immediately vanquished him with ease.

Then said Sir Bors de Ganis, "I never knew Cornish knight of so great valor, nor so valiant, as that knight who beareth the trappings embroidered with crowns."

After this, Sir Tristram and Sir Dinadan left them and rode into a forest, and here a damsel met them, who came for the love of Sir Lancelot to seek after some noble knights of King Arthur's Court, to rescue Sir Lancelot. For Queen Morgan le Fay, the wicked sorceress, had resolved by treachery to slay Sir Lancelot, and for that cause she ordained thirty knights to lie in wait for him. This damsel knew of the treachery, and this was the reason she came to seek noble knights to help Sir Lancelot. For that night, or the day after, Sir Lancelot would come where those thirty knights were.

The damsel met first Sir Bors, Sir Bleoberis, Sir Ector, and Sir Driant, and she told them all four of the treason of Morgan le Fay. They promised her that they would be near where Sir Lancelot should meet with the thirty knights, and if so be these set on him, they would rescue him as well as they could. After leaving the four knights the damsel by chance met Sir Tristram and Sir Dinadan, and these also she told of all the treachery that was ordained for Sir Lancelot.

"Fair damsel," said Sir Tristram, "lead me to the place where they expect to meet with Sir Lancelot."

"What will ye do?" said Sir Dinadan. "It is not for us to fight with thirty knights, and wit ye well, I will not do so. To match one knight, two or three are enough, if they be men. But to match fifteen knights that will I never undertake."

"Fie, for shame," said Sir Tristram, "do but your part."

"Nay," said Dinadan, "I will not do so unless you will lend me your shield; for ye bear a shield of Cornwall, and because of the cowardice that is named to the knights of Cornwall, by your shields ye are ever avoided."

"Nay, I will not part from my shield, for her sake who gave it me," said Tristram. "But one thing I promise thee, Sir Dinadan, if thou abide not with me, I shall slay thee here. For I desire no more of thee but to answer one knight, and if thy heart will not serve thee, stand by, and look upon me and them."

"Sir," said the cowardly Dinadan, "I promise you to look on, and do what I can to save myself, but I wish I had not met with you."

Soon after, the thirty knights drew near the four knights, and they were all aware of each other. But the thirty knights let the four knights pass, in case they too, had been ordered to attack Sir Lancelot; and the four knights let the thirty knights pass, with the intention of seeing what they would do with Sir Lancelot.

So the thirty knights passed on, and came up to Sir Tristram and Sir Dinadan. And as they drew near Sir Tristram cried aloud:

"Lo, here is a knight against you for the love of Sir Lancelot!"

And there he slew two with one spear, and ten with his sword; and then Sir Dinadan, plucking up courage, rushed into the fray, and did passing well.

So of the thirty knights there went but ten away, and these fled.

Sir Bors de Ganis and his three companions watched this battle, and they saw well it was the same knight who had jousted with them near the sea. Then they took their horses, and rode to Sir Tristram, and praised him, and thanked him for his good deeds; and they all wanted Sir Tristram to go with them to their lodgings.

But he said nay, he would go to no lodging.

Then all the four knights prayed him to tell them his name.

"Fair lords," said Tristram, "I will not tell you my name at present."

THE FALSE TREASON OF MORGAN LE FAY

Sɪʀ Tristram and Sir Dinadan continued on their way, and as they went they had many adventures. But Sir Dinadan lamented all the while that ever he fell into Sir Tristram's company. For every knight they met wanted to joust with them, and Sir Dinadan liked not so much fighting, and moreover he had many falls.

"Ye fare as a madman," he said to Sir Tristram, "and as a man who is out of his mind, who would cast himself away; I could curse the time that ever I saw you. For in all the world there are not two knights that are so mad as Sir Lancelot and you. For once I fell into the fellowship of Sir Lancelot, as I have now done with you, and he set me such a work that I kept my bed a quarter of a year. Defend me from two such knights, and especially from *your* companionship!"

They found lodging that night with a good man in a priory, where they were well treated. On the morrow Sir Tristram departed, leaving Sir Dinadan in the priory, for the latter was so weary and so sorely bruised that he could not ride. The next day Sir Tristram met with messengers, and they told him there was great proclamation made of a tournament between King Carados of Scotland and the King of North Wales, and that they were to joust against each other at the Castle of Maidens. These messengers were searching all the country after good knights, and in especial King Carados was seeking for Sir Lancelot, and the King of North Wales was seeking for Sir Tristram of Lyonesse.

So Sir Tristram thought he would be at that tournament.

The same day he met with a damsel, who told him he should win great renown from a knight adventurous, who did much harm in all that country. When Sir Tristram heard her say so, he was glad to go with her, to win honor. They had ridden about six miles when Sir Gawaine met them. He knew the damsel immediately, that she was one of the ladies of the wicked Queen, Morgan le Fay.

"Fair knight," said Sir Gawaine, "whither ride you now with that damsel?"

"Sir," said Tristram, "I know not whither I shall ride, only as the damsel shall lead me."

"Sir," said Gawaine, "ye shall not ride with her, for she and her lady never did good, but ill." Then pulling out his sword, he said, "Damsel, unless thou tell me quickly for what cause thou leadest this knight with you, thou shalt die for it at once. I know all your lady's treason and yours."

"Mercy, Sir Gawaine!" she cried, "and if ye will save my life, I will tell you."

"Say on, and thou shalt have thy life," said Gawaine.

"Sir, Queen Morgan le Fay, my lady, hath ordained thirty ladies to seek and spy after Sir Lancelot or Sir Tristram, and by a plot with these ladies, whoever first meets with either of these two knights, they shall turn them to Morgan le Fay's Castle, saying they shall do deeds of worship. And if either of these two knights comes there, there are thirty knights lying and watching in a tower, to wait for Sir Lancelot or Sir Tristram."

"Fie for shame," said Sir Gawaine, "that ever such false treason should be wrought or used by a Queen,—a King's sister, and the daughter of a King and Queen."

Then Sir Gawaine and Sir Tristram agreed to ride to the Castle where Morgan le Fay was, and to defy the malice of the thirty knights. And Sir Gawaine kept on thinking that his companion must certainly be Tristram of Lyonesse, for he had heard tell how two knights had slain and beaten thirty knights.

When they came before the Castle Sir Gawaine cried out in a high voice:

"Queen Morgan le Fay, send out your knights whom ye have laid to watch for Sir Lancelot and Sir Tristram! Now I know your false treason and through all places where I ride men shall know of your false treason. And now, ye thirty knights, let Sir Gawaine see if ye dare come out of your Castle!"

Then the Queen and all the thirty knights spoke at once, and said:

"Sir Gawaine, full well thou knowest what thou dost, and sayest, for we know thee passing well. But all that thou speakest and dost, thou sayest it from pride of that good knight who is there with thee. For there be some of us who know full well the hands of that knight, and wit ye well, Sir Gawaine, it is more for his sake than for thine that we will not come out of this Castle. As for that knight who beareth the arms of Cornwall, we know him and what he is."

Finding that Queen Morgan le Fay and her thirty knights were too cowardly to face them openly, Sir Gawaine and Sir Tristram departed from the Castle, and rode on their travels a day or two together.

They had not gone far before they saw a cruel knight

chasing a lady to slay her, for he had already slain her lover. His name was called "Sir Breuse Without Pity."

"Hold still," said Sir Gawaine, "and do not show forth, and ye shall see me reward yonder false knight. For if he espy you, he is so well horsed that he will escape away."

Then Sir Gawaine rode between Sir Breuse and the lady, calling out, "False knight, leave her, and deal with me!"

Sir Breuse, seeing no one but Sir Gawaine, levelled his spear, and Sir Gawaine did the same, and there Sir Breuse overthrew Sir Gawaine; then as the knight lay on the ground he rode over and across him several times, to destroy him. When Sir Tristram saw him do so villainous a deed he hurled out against him.

As soon as Sir Breuse saw the shield of Cornwall, he knew well it was Sir Tristram, and away he fled, with Sir Tristram after him. Sir Breuse had so good a horse that he got quite away, but Tristram followed him for a long time, for he would fain have been avenged on him.

After chasing him some way, he saw a fair well, and thither he rode to rest. Alighting from his horse, he tied him to a tree, and pulling off his helm, he washed his face and hands, and presently he fell asleep.

In the meanwhile came a damsel who had sought Sir Tristram many days and many ways in that country. When she came to the well she looked at the sleeping knight, but she would not have remembered him for Sir Tristram, if it had not been for his horse, "Passe-Brewel." By this she knew him; for when he was mad in the forest, Sir Fergus, a knight of King Mark's Court, took care of the horse, and there this lady, who was no other than Dame Bragwaine, had often seen him.

Dame Bragwaine stayed still until Tristram awoke and

then she saluted him, and he her again, for they were of old acquaintance. She told him how she had sought him far and wide, and how she had letters from Queen Iseult of Cornwall. Tristram read them at once, and very glad he was to have them.

"Lady Bragwaine," he said, "ye shall ride with me till that tournament at the Castle of Maidens is over; and then ye shall bear letters and tidings back to Queen Iseult."

AT THE CASTLE OF MAIDENS

ON the first day of the great tournament at the Castle of Maidens Sir Tristram did so gallantly and overthrew so many knights that King Arthur and all the Kings and lords who were judges gave him the prize, although they knew him not, but named him the "Knight with the Black Shield."

On the morrow, Sir Palamides, who had been fighting for the King of North Wales, left him, and rode to King Arthur's side, where was King Carados, and the King of Ireland and Sir Lancelot's kin, and Sir Gawaine's kin. And the better to disguise themselves, Sir Lancelot and thirty-two knights of his blood had assumed shields of Cornwall. Sir Palamides sent a damsel as messenger to Sir Tristram to ask who he was, and what was his name.

"As to that," said Sir Tristram, "tell Sir Palamides he shall not know at this time, nor until I have broken two spears on him. But tell him plainly that side on which he is, I will be on the contrary side."

"Sir," said the damsel, "ye shall understand that Sir Palamides will be on King Arthur's side, where the most noble knights of the world be."

"Then," said Sir Tristram, "I will be with the King of North Wales, because Sir Palamides is on King Arthur's side, else I would not be so, except for his sake."

When King Arthur came, the trumpets blew for the field, and then began a great fight; King Carados jousted with the King of North Wales, and there had a fall, whereupon other knights of King Arthur's immediately rushed in, and beat back the knights of the King of North Wales. Then Sir Tristram rode in, and began so roughly and so hugely that no one could withstand him, and thus he kept on for a long time. But at the last Tristram fell among the company of King Ban, and was attacked by Sir Bors de Ganis, Sir Ector de Maris, Sir Blamor de Ganis, and many other knights. Sir Tristram smote on the right hand, and on the left hand, so that all lords and ladies spoke of his noble deeds. But in the end he would have had the worse, had it not been for the King with the Hundred Knights, who came with his followers, and rescued Sir Tristram, and carried him away from those knights who bore the shields of Cornwall.

After this, Sir Tristram saw another troop by themselves, about forty knights together, and Sir Kay, the Steward, was their governor. Sir Tristram rode in amongst them, and smote down Sir Kay from his horse, and there he fared among those knights like a greyhound among cronies.

Sir Lancelot, meanwhile, found a knight who was sorely wounded on the head; he asked him who had done it.

"Sir," he said, "a knight who beareth a black shield. I could curse the time that ever I met with him, for he is a devil, and no man."

Sir Lancelot left him, and hoping to meet with Sir Tristram, he rode seeking him, with his sword drawn in his hand; at last he espied him, how he hurled here and there, and at every stroke Sir Tristram well-nigh smote down a knight.

"Oh, mercy," said King Arthur, "since the time I bore

arms, I never saw knight do such marvellous deeds of valor."

"And if I should assail this knight," said Sir Lancelot to himself, "I should shame myself," and therewith he put up his sword.

The King with a Hundred Knights, and a hundred more men of North Wales, now set upon twenty of Sir Lancelot's kin, and those twenty knights held ever together, and none would fail the other. When Sir Tristram saw the noblesse of these twenty knights he marvelled at their good deeds, for he saw by their bearing and conduct that they would rather die than yield the field.

"Now," said Sir Tristram, "well may he be valiant and full of prowess that hath such noble knights for his kin, and full like is he to be a noble man who is their leader and governor!" He meant by this, Sir Lancelot of the Lake.

After Sir Tristram had watched them for a long time, he thought it shame to see two hundred knights battering upon twenty knights, so he rode to the King of North Wales and said:

"Sir, leave your fighting with those twenty knights, for ye win no renown from them, ye be so many, and they be so few; and wit ye well they will not leave the field, I see by their cheer and countenance; and honor ye get none, if ye slay them. Therefore leave your fighting with them, for I, to increase my honor, will ride to the twenty knights and help them with all my might and power."

"Nay," said the King of North Wales, "ye shall not do so. Now that I see your courage and courtesy, to please you I will withdraw my knights, for evermore a good knight will favor another, and like will draw to like."

Then the King of North Wales withdrew his knights.

All this while and long before, Sir Lancelot had watched Sir Tristram with the very purpose of having fellowship with him. But suddenly Sir Tristram, Sir Dinadan, and Gouvernail his man rode their way into the forest, so that no man perceived where they went.

Then King Arthur blew for the fighting to cease, and gave the King of North Wales the prize, because Sir Tristram was on his side. Sir Lancelot rode here and there like a raging lion, because he had lost Sir Tristram, but he had to return without him to King Arthur. Then in all the field there was a noise that with the wind might have been heard two miles off, how the lords and ladies cried:

"The Knight with the Black Shield has won the field!"

"Alas," said King Arthur, "what has become of that knight? It is shame to all those in the field so to let him escape away from you, but with gentleness and courtesy ye might have brought him unto me to the Castle of Maidens."

Afterwards the noble King Arthur went to his knights and comforted them in the best way he could for having been defeated that day. Many were hurt and sore wounded, but many were also unhurt.

"My brave knights," he said, "be not dismayed, even although ye have lost the field this day. Look that ye be of good cheer, for tomorrow I will be in the field with you, and revenge you of your enemies."

THE THIRD DAY OF THE TOURNAMENT

THEN on the morrow the trumpets blew to the tournament for the third day.

The King of North Wales, and the King with the Hundred Knights, encountered with King Carados and with the King of Ireland; and there the King with the Hundred Knights smote down King Carados, and the King of North Wales smote down the King of Ireland. Sir Palamides came at once to the help of the fallen knights, and made great work, for by his indented shield he was well known. Then King Arthur joined him, and did great deeds of arms, and put the King of North Wales and the King of the Hundred Knights to the worse. But Sir Tristram with his black shield came to their help, and quickly he jousted with Sir Palamides, and there by fine force he smote Sir Palamides over his horse's croup.

Then cried King Arthur, "Knight with the Black Shield, make thee ready to me!" and in the same wise Sir Tristram smote King Arthur.

By force of Arthur's knights, the King and Sir Palamides were horsed again, and the King with an eager heart, seizing a spear, smote Sir Tristram from one side over his horse. Hot-foot, from the other side, Sir Palamides came upon Sir Tristram, as he was on foot, meaning to over-ride him, but Sir Tristram was aware of him, and stepped aside, and with great ire he got him by the arm, and pulled him down from his horse.

Sir Palamides arose lightly, and they dashed together mightily with their swords, and many Kings, Queens, and lords stood and beheld them. At the last, Sir Tristram smote Sir Palamides upon the helm three mighty strokes, and at every stroke he gave him, he cried, "Have this for Sir Tristram's sake!" With that, Sir Palamides fell to the earth, grovelling.

Then came the King of the Hundred Knights, and brought Sir Tristram a horse, and so he was mounted again. Then he was aware of King Arthur with a naked sword in his hand, and with his spear Sir Tristram ran upon King Arthur; the King boldly awaited him, and with his sword he smote the spear in two. At this Sir Tristram was so astonished that King Arthur gave him three or four great strokes before he could get out his sword, but at last Sir Tristram drew his sword, and assailed the other, pressing hard.

Now the great crowd parted them; then Sir Tristram rode here and there, and fought with such fury that eleven of the good knights of the blood of King Ban, who were Sir Lancelot's kin, were that day smitten down by Sir Tristram. All people, of every estate, marvelled at his great deeds, and all shouted for "the Knight with the Black Shield!"

The uproar was so great that Sir Lancelot heard it, and getting a great spear he came towards the shouting.

"Knight of the Black Shield, make thee ready to joust with me!" cried Sir Lancelot.

When Sir Tristram heard him say this, he took spear in hand, and both lowered their heads, and came together like thunder; Sir Tristram's spear broke in pieces, and Sir Lancelot by ill fortune struck Sir Tristram on the side, a deep wound nigh to death. But yet Sir Tristram left not his saddle, and so the spear broke; though sorely wounded, Tristram got out his sword and rushed at Sir Lancelot and gave him three great strokes on the helm, so that sparks flew out, and Sir Lancelot lowered his head down to his saddle-bow. And therewithal Sir Tristram departed from the field, for he felt himself so wounded that he thought he should have died.

Sir Dinadan espied him go, and followed him into the forest. After they had gone some way, Sir Tristram alighted, and unlaced his harness, and dressed his wound. Then Sir Dinadan feared that he would have died.

"Nay, nay, Dinadan, never dread thee," said Sir Tristram, "for I am heart whole, and of this wound I shall soon be healed, by the mercy of God."

When Sir Tristram departed into the forest, Sir Lancelot held always the fight, like a man enraged, who took no heed of himself, and wit ye well, there was many a noble knight against him. King Arthur, seeing Sir Lancelot do such marvellous deeds of arms, armed himself, and taking his horse and armor, rode into the field, to help Sir Lancelot, and many other knights came in with King Arthur. To make a short tale, in conclusion, the King of North Wales and the King of the Hundred Knights were put to the worse, and because Sir Lancelot abode, and was the last in the field, the prize was given him.

Sir Lancelot, however, would not for King, Queen, nor knight accept the prize; but wherever the cry was cried through the field, "Sir Lancelot, Sir Lancelot hath won the field this day!" Sir Lancelot had another contrary cry made, —"Sir Tristram hath won the field! For he began first, and last he hath endured! And so hath done the first day, the second, and the third day!"

THE QUEST OF THE TEN KNIGHTS

THEN everyone, high and low, said great things of Sir Lancelot for the honor he did Sir Tristram, and because of that honor done to Sir Tristram, he was at that time more praised and renowned than if he had overthrown five hundred knights; and all the people, solely because of this courtesy, first the nobles, great and small, and afterwards all the common folk, cried at once, "Sir Lancelot hath won the field, whosoever say nay!" At this Lancelot was angry and ashamed, and therewith he rode to King Arthur.

"Alas!" said the King, "we are all dismayed that Sir Tristram is thus departed from us. Truly he is one of the noblest knights that ever I saw hold spear or sword in hand."

King Arthur and Sir Lancelot took their horses to seek Sir Tristram, but when they came to the pavilion where he had slept the night before the tournament, he and Sir Dinadan were gone. They were very sorry at not finding him, and returned to the Castle of Maidens, making great dole for the hurt of Sir Tristram, and his sudden departing.

"Truly," said King Arthur, "I am more grieved that I cannot meet with him than for all the hurts that all my knights have had at the tournament."

Right so came Sir Gaheris, and told King Arthur that after Sir Tristram was wounded Sir Palamides had gone after him into the forest, and challenged him to joust, and that Sir Tristram had there smitten him down.

"Alas," said King Arthur, "that was great dishonor to Sir Palamides, inasmuch as Sir Tristram was sorely wounded, and now may we all, Kings, knights, and men of worship, say that Sir Tristram may be called a noble knight, and one of the best knights I ever saw in the days of my life. For I will that ye all know, that I never saw knight do so marvellously as he hath done these three days; for he was the first who began, and the longest who held on, save this last day. And though he was hurt, it was a manly adventure of two noble knights; and when two noble men encounter, it must needs be that one will have the worst, as God may allow at the time."

"As for me," said Sir Lancelot, "for all the lands that ever my father left me, I would not have hurt Sir Tristram, if I had known him at that time. That I hurt him was because I saw not his shield, for if I had seen his black shield I would not have meddled with him for many causes, for he did lately for me as much as ever knight did; and it is well known that he had ado with thirty knights, and no help save Sir Dinadan. And one thing I shall promise,—Sir Palamides shall repent it for his unkindly dealing in following that noble knight, whom I by mishap hurt thus." So spoke Sir Lancelot all the honor he could concerning Sir Tristram.

Then King Arthur made a great feast to all that would come, and at the feast he said to Sir Lancelot:

"Had it not been for you we had not lost Sir Tristram, for he was here daily until the time ye met with him, and in an evil hour ye encountered with him."

"My lord Arthur," said Lancelot, "you accuse me that I am the cause of his departure: truly it was against my will.

But when men be hot in deeds of arms, often they hurt their friends as well as their foes; and, my lord, ye shall understand Sir Tristram is a man I am loath to offend, for he has done for me more than ever as yet I have done for him."

Then Sir Lancelot made them bring forth a book, and he said:

"Here we are, ten knights, who will swear upon a book never to rest one night where we rest another, this twelve months, until we find Sir Tristram. And as for me, I promise you upon this book that if I meet with him, by fair means or foul, I shall bring him to this Court, or else I shall die for it."

The names of the ten knights who undertook this quest were these following:—First was Sir Lancelot; then Sir Ector de Maris, Sir Bors de Ganis, Bleoberis, and Sir Blamor de Ganis; Lucan, the butler; Sir Uwaine, Sir Galihud, Sir Lionel, and Galiodin.

These ten noble knights departed from the Court of King Arthur, and thus they rode upon their quest together, until they came to a cross, where parted four highways; and there the fellowship broke up into four parties, to seek Sir Tristram.

In the meanwhile, Sir Tristram and Sir Dinadan were lodging in the Castle of an old knight called Sir Darras.

Sir Palamides after his fall in the forest was nearly out of his wits with rage against Sir Tristram, so he resolved to follow him. Coming to a river, in his madness he tried to make his horse leap over, but his horse failed footing, and fell into the river, wherefore Sir Palamides dreaded lest he should be drowned. However, he got clear from his horse, and swam to the land, but the horse went down into the water.

When Sir Palamides reached the land he took off his

armor, and sat roaring and crying like a man out of his mind. Right so came a damsel past Sir Palamides, and he and she had language together, which pleased neither of them; so the damsel rode her way till she came to the place where Tristram was lodging with an old knight, and there she told him how by chance she had met with the maddest knight that ever she met withal.

"What bare he in his shield?" said Sir Tristram.

"It was indented with white and black," said the damsel.

"Ah," said Sir Tristram, "that is Sir Palamides, the good knight, for well I know him for one of the best knights living in this realm."

Then the old knight took a little hackney, and rode for Sir Palamides, and brought him unto his own Manor.

Whenever Sir Palamides saw Sir Tristram, he looked at him curiously, for although he did not recognize him, it seemed to him he had seen him before. Then he would say to Sir Dinadan, "If ever I may meet with Sir Tristram, he shall not escape my hands."

"I marvel," said Sir Dinadan, "that ye boast behind Sir Tristram's back, for it is but lately he was in your hands, and ye in his hands. Why would ye not hold him when ye had him? For I myself saw twice or thrice that ye got but little worship of Sir Tristram."

Then was Sir Palamides ashamed.

Thus they stayed for awhile in the Castle with the old Knight, Sir Darras. But one day there came a damsel who told Sir Darras that three of his sons had been slain at the tournament of the Castle of Maidens, and two grievously wounded, so that they were never likely to help themselves, and all this was done by a noble knight who bare a black shield. Then someone else said that the same knight who bare the black shield was now within that very Castle. Sir Darras went to Tristram's chamber, and there he found his shield, and showed it to the damsel.

"Ah, sir," said the damsel, "the same man who bore that shield is he who slew your three sons."

Without tarrying, Sir Darras at once threw Sir Tristram, and Sir Palamides, and Sir Dinadan into a strong prison, and there Sir Tristram fell so ill that he nearly died. And every day Sir Palamides would reproach Sir Tristram, because of the old hate betwixt them, and always Sir Tristram spoke fair, and said little. But when Palamides saw him fall sick, then he was sorry for him, and comforted him in all the best wise he could.

Then came forty knights to Sir Darras, who were of his own kin, and they would have slain Sir Tristram and his two companions; Sir Darras, however, would not suffer that, although he kept them still in prison; and they had sufficient meat and drink.

But Sir Tristram endured there great pain, for sickness overtook him, and that is the greatest pain a prisoner can have. For all the while a prisoner has his health of body, he can endure, by the mercy of God, and in hope of deliverance; but when sickness toucheth a prisoner's body, then may a prisoner say all wealth is bereft him, and then he hath cause to wail and to weep. And so did Sir Tristram, when sickness overtook him, for then he had such sorrow that he almost slew himself.

THE STRANGE SHIELD OF MORGAN LE FAY

WHEN Sir Tristram fell so ill, Sir Dinadan and Sir Palamides made great sorrow, and one day a damsel came and found them mourning. So she went to Sir Darras, and told him how the mighty knight who bore the black shield was likely to die.

"That shall not be," said Sir Darras, "for God forbid that when any knights come to me for succor I should suffer them to die within my prison. Therefore, fetch that knight and his companions before me." And when he saw Tristram he said, "Sir Knight, I repent me of thy sickness, for thou art called a full noble knight, and so thou seemest, for thou art well it shall never be said that Sir Darras shall destroy such a noble knight as thou art, in prison, howbeit thou hast slain three of my sons, whereby I was greatly aggrieved. But now thou shalt go, and thy companions; your armor and horses have been fair and clean kept, and ye shall go where ye like —upon this covenant, that thou, knight, will promise me to be good friends to my two sons who are now alive, and also that thou tell me thy name."

"Sir," said he, "as for me, my name is Sir Tristram of Lyonesse, and in Cornwall was I born, and I am nephew to King Mark. And as for the death of your sons I could not help it, for if they had been the next kin that I have, I could not have done otherwise. If indeed I had slain them by treason or treachery, I had been worthy to have died."

"All this I consider," said Sir Darras, "that all ye did was by force of knighthood, and that was the cause why I would not put you to death. But since ye be Sir Tristram, the noble knight, I pray you heartily to be a good friend to me and to my sons."

"Sir," said Tristram, "I promise you by the faith of my body I will do you service as long as I live, for ye have done to us only as a knight would naturally do."

Sir Tristram rested in the Castle till his sickness mended, and when he was well again and strong the three companions made ready to leave; every knight took his horse, and so they departed, riding together till they came to a cross-way, where they each went a different road.

It happened by chance that Sir Tristram came to ask for lodging at a Castle where Morgan le Fay was, and there that night he had good cheer. On the morrow when he would have departed the Queen said:

"Wit ye well, ye shall not depart lightly, for ye are here as a prisoner."

"God forbid," said Sir Tristram, "for I was but lately a prisoner."

"Fair knight," said the Queen, "ye shall abide with me till I know what you are, and whence you come. Tell me your name, and I will suffer you to depart when you will."

"Upon that covenant I will tell you my name—it is Sir Tristram of Lyonesse."

"Ah," said Morgan le Fay, "if I had known that, ye should not have departed so soon, but since I have made a promise I will keep it, on condition that you will promise me to bear a shield that I shall deliver you, unto the Castle of the Hard

Rock, where King Arthur hath proclaimed a great tournament; and I pray you to go there, and do for me as much deeds of arms as ye can do. For at the Castle of Maidens, Sir Tristram, ye did marvellous deeds of arms as ever I heard of knight doing."

"Madam," said Tristram, "let me see the shield that I shall bear."

So the shield was brought forth, and it was goldish, with a King and Queen painted therein, and a knight standing above them, with one foot on the King's head, and the other upon the Queen's.

"Madam," said Tristram, "this is a fair shield and a mighty; but what signifieth this King and this Queen, and that knight standing upon both their heads?"

"I will tell you," said Morgan le Fay; "it signifieth King Arthur and Queen Guinevere, and a knight that holdeth them both in bondage."

"Who is that knight?" asked Tristram.

"That ye shall not know just yet," said the Queen.

But it was a wicked device of Morgan le Fay to bring trouble on Sir Lancelot, out of revenge, because he would never love her, nor do anything at her request. She hoped King Arthur would see the shield, and be angry with Sir Lancelot because of the picture on it.

Sir Tristram took the shield, and promised Morgan le Fay to bear it at the tournament at the Castle of the Hard Rock. He knew not at that time that the shield was ordained to work mischief against Sir Lancelot, but afterwards he knew it. Taking leave of the Queen, he rode to the Castle, where he saw five hundred tents. The King of Scots and the King of Ireland held against King Arthur's knights, and there began a great *melee*. Sir Tristram rushed into the fray, and did marvellous deeds of arms, smiting down many knights. And always in the front of the fight shone that strange shield.

When the King saw it he marvelled greatly with what intent it had been made, but Queen Guinevere guessed what it was, wherefore she was heavy-hearted. A damsel of Queen Morgan le Fay's happened to be present in the chamber from which the King watched the tournament, and when she heard him speak of the shield, she said openly:

"Sir King, wit ye well that this shield was ordained for you, to show you shame and dishonor," and then she stole away secretly, so that no man knew what became of her.

King Arthur was sad and wroth at her words, and asked from whence came that damsel, but there was no one who knew her, nor where she went.

All this while the King watched Sir Tristram, who did such marvellous deeds of arms, that he wondered sorely what knight he could be, for he knew well it was not Sir Lancelot. He was told that Sir Tristram was in Brittany with his wife, Iseult of the White Hands, for if he had been in England Arthur thought Sir Lancelot or some of his companions who had gone in quest of Sir Tristram would have found him before now. So King Arthur marvelled what knight this could be, and he kept always gazing at the shield.

Then Sir Tristram smote down knights, wonderful to behold, on the right hand, and on the left hand, scarcely a knight could withstand him. But the King of Scots and the King of Ireland began to withdraw themselves. Arthur, seeing this, resolved that the knight with the strange shield should not escape him. Therefore he called Sir Uwaine, and bade him arm him, and make him ready; and they quickly appeared before Sir Tristram, and challenged him to tell them where he had that shield.

"Sir," he said, "I had it of Queen Morgan le Fay, sister to King Arthur."

"If so be you can describe what you bear, you are worthy to bear the arms."

"As for that," said Sir Tristram, "I will answer you. This shield was given me, not desired, of Queen Morgan le Fay. And as for me, I cannot describe these arms, for it is no point of my charge; and yet I trust to bear them with honor."

"Truly," said King Arthur, "you ought to bear no arms, unless you know what you bear. But I pray you tell me your name."

"To what intent?" said Sir Tristram.

"Because I wish to know it," said King Arthur.

"Sir, ye shall not know it at this time."

"Then shall you and I do battle together," said King Arthur.

"Why will you do battle with me unless I tell you my name?" said Tristram. "You need hardly do that, if you were a man of honor, for you have seen me this day have great travail; therefore you are an unworthy knight to ask battle of me, considering my great travail. However, I will not fail you, and do not imagine that I fear you; though you think you have me at a great advantage, yet I shall endure right well."

Therewith King Arthur dressed his shield and his spear, and Sir Tristram against him, and they came so eagerly together that King Arthur broke his spear to pieces upon Sir Tristram's shield. But Sir Tristram hit King Arthur again, so that horse and man fell to the earth; and the King was wounded on the left side, a great wound and a perilous.

When Sir Uwaine saw his lord Arthur lie on the ground

sore wounded, he was passing heavy. Then he dressed his shield and spear, and cried aloud to Sir Tristram, "Knight, defend thee!" They came together like thunder, and Sir Uwaine broke his spear to pieces on Tristram's shield. And Sir Tristram smote him harder and sorer, with such might that he bore him clean out of his saddle to the earth.

With that, Sir Tristram turned about, and said:

"Fair knights, I had no need to joust with you, for I have had enough to do this day."

Then Arthur arose, and went to Sir Uwaine, and said to Sir Tristram:

"We have as we have deserved, for through our pride we demanded battle of you, and yet we know not your name."

"Nevertheless," said Sir Uwaine, "by my faith, he is as strong a knight, in my opinion, as any now living."

THE TOMBSTONE
BY THE RIVER OF CAMELOT

AFTER overthrowing King Arthur and Sir Uwaine, Sir Tristram departed from the Castle of the Hard Rock; everywhere he went he asked after Sir Lancelot, but in no place could he hear of him, whether he were dead or alive, wherefore Sir Tristram made great dole and sorrow. As he rode by a forest he was aware of a fair tower with a marsh on the one side, and a green meadow on the other, and there he saw ten knights fighting together. As he came nearer, he saw how it was but one knight, who did battle against nine knights, and that one knight did so marvellously that Tristram wondered greatly how one knight could do such deeds of arms. He had great pity for him, and by his shield he thought it must be Sir Palamides.

So he rode to the knights, and cried to them, and bade them cease their battle, for they did themselves great shame, so many knights to fight with one. It was a pity, he said, that so good a knight should be slain so cowardly, and therefore he warned them, he would succor him with all his prowess.

The master of the party, who was called "Breuse Without Pity," the most mischievous knight then living, scornfully defied Sir Tristram, but when his men felt Sir Tristram's strokes they all fled into the tower, and though Tristram followed fast after, with his sword in his hand, they escaped, and shut him outside the gate.

Sir Tristram returned to the knight he had rescued, and found him sitting under a tree, sore wounded.

"Great thanks to you for your goodness," said the knight, "for you have saved my life."

"What is your name?" said Tristram.

He answered that it was Palamides.

"Oh," said Sir Tristram; "thou hast had a fair favor of me this day that I should rescue thee, and thou art the man in the world whom I most hate! But now make ready, for I will do battle with thee."

"What is your name?" said Palamides.

"My name is Sir Tristram, your mortal enemy."

"It may be so," said Sir Palamides, "but ye have done overmuch for me this day that I should fight with you; for inasmuch as ye have saved my life it will be no honor for you to have ado with me, for ye are fresh, and I am wounded sore. Therefore, if ye will need have ado with me, assign me a day, and then I shall meet·you without fail."

"Ye say well," said Sir Tristram. "Now I assign you to meet me, to do battle with me, this day fortnight, in the meadow by the river of Camelot, where Merlin set the tombstone."

"I shall not fail you," said Sir Palamides.

Thus they were agreed, and so they departed, each taking a different way.

At the time appointed Sir Tristram rode straight to Camelot, to the tomb where Merlin had made long before on the spot where the brave knight Lanceor and his fair lady Columbe were both buried under one stone. And at that time Merlin prophesied that in that same place should fight two of the best knights that were ever in Arthur's days.

When Tristram came to the tomb where Lanceor and his

lady were buried he looked about him for Sir Palamides. Then he was aware of a comely knight who came riding against him, all in white, with a covered shield. When he came near, Sir Tristram cried, "Ye be welcome, Sir Knight, and well and truly have you kept your promise."

Then they dressed their shields and spear, and came together with all the might of their horses. They met so fiercely that both horses and knights fell to the earth, but freeing themselves as swiftly as they could, they struck together with bright swords, and each wounded the other sorely. Thus they fought for a long while, and many great pieces were hewn out of their armor, but never one word was uttered by either of them.

At last the knight clad in white spoke, and said:

"Knight, thou fightest wonderly well, as ever I saw knight, therefore, if it please you, tell me your name."

"Sir," said Tristram, "I am loath to tell any man my name."

"Truly," said the stranger, "if ever I were required, I was never loath to tell my name."

"It is well said," quoth Tristram; "then I require you to tell me your name."

"Fair Knight," said he, "my name is Sir Lancelot of the Lake."

"Alas," said Tristram, "what have I done? For you are the man in the world I love the best."

"Fair Knight," said he, "tell me your name."

"Truly, my name is Sir Tristram."

"Oh," said Sir Lancelot, "what adventure is befallen me!" And therewith he knelt down and yielded up his sword to Tristram. But Tristram, too, knelt down, and yielded his sword to Lancelot, thus each gave the other the honor.

Then forthwith they went to the tombstone, and sat down

on it, and took off their helms, and kissed each other. And afterwards they rode to Camelot.

As they came near they met Sir Gawaine and Sir Gaheris, who had promised King Arthur never to come again to the Court till they brought Sir Tristram with them.

"Return again," said Lancelot, "for your quest is done, for I have met with Sir Tristram. Lo, here is he in person!"

Then was Sir Gawaine glad. "Ye are welcome," he said to Tristram, "for now have ye eased me greatly of my labor. For what cause came ye to this Court?"

"Fair sir," said Tristram, "I came into this country because of Sir Palamides, for he and I had assigned at this day to have done battle together at the tombstone in the meadow by the river of Camelot. And thus by chance my lord Sir Lancelot and I met together."

At this moment came King Arthur, and when he knew that Sir Tristram was there, he ran to him, and taking him by the hand, said, "Sir Tristram, ye be as welcome as any knight that ever came to this Court," and so he led him to the Round Table.

Then came Queen Guinevere, and many ladies with her, and all the ladies said with one voice, "Welcome, Sir Tristram!"

"Welcome!" said the damsels; "Welcome!" said the knights.

"Welcome," said Arthur, "for one of the best knights and the gentlest of the world, and the man of most renown! For of all manner of hunting thou bearest the prize; and of all the terms of hunting and hawking thou art the beginner; in all instruments of music, thou art the most skilled. Therefore, gentle knight," said Arthur, "thou art welcome to this Court! Also, I pray thee, grant me a boon."

"It shall be at your command," said Tristram.

"Well," said Arthur, "I desire of you that ye will abide in my Court."

"Sir," said Tristram, "I am loath to do that, for I have ado in many countries."

"Not so," said Arthur; "ye have promised it me; ye cannot say nay."

"Sir, I will do as ye will," said Tristram.

Arthur went to the seats about the Round Table, and looked in all the seats where knights were lacking. Then the King saw in the seat of Sir Marhaus letters which said:

"This is the seat of the noble knight, Sir Tristram."

So with great splendor and feasting, King Arthur made Sir Tristram Knight of the Round Table.

KING FOX

OUT OF CORNWALL INTO ENGLAND

"KING FOX" was the name given by Sir Lancelot to the sly and wicked King Mark of Cornwall, which was as much to say, "He fareth all by wiles and treachery." Now we shall see how well-deserved was this scornful nickname.

King Mark had great spite and envy because of the renown of his nephew Sir Tristram, and therefore chased him out of Cornwall; and in especial he was jealous and suspicious because his wife, the beautiful Queen Iseult, and Sir Tristram, who had been friends long ago, always loved each other dearly. When Tristram departed out of Cornwall into England, King Mark heard of the prowess he did there, which grieved him sorely. Both he and the Queen secretly sent separate spies to the Court of King Arthur to find out what deeds Tristram did. When the messengers came home they told the truth as they had heard, that Tristram surpassed all other knights, unless it were Sir Lancelot. King Mark was right heavy at these tidings, and La Belle Iseult, on the other hand, was just as glad.

In great displeasure, King Mark took with him two good knights and two squires, and went his way into England, with the intent of slaying Sir Tristram. One of these knights was named Sir Bersules, the other was called Sir Amant. As they rode, King Mark asked a knight whom he met where he should find King Arthur. He said, at Camelot. Also he asked the knight after Sir Tristram, whether he had heard of him in the Court of King Arthur.

"Wit ye well," said the knight, "ye shall find Sir Tristram there for a man of as great worship as any now alive, for through his prowess he won the tournament of the Castle of Maidens that standeth by the Hard Rock. And since then he hath vanquished with his own hands thirty knights, men of great honor. And the last battle ever he did, was fought with Sir Lancelot, and that was a marvellous battle. And Sir Lancelot brought Sir Tristram, not by force, to the Court, whereat King Arthur rejoiced greatly, and so made him Knight of the Round Table, and his seat is where the good knight, Sir Marhaus's, seat was."

King Mark was much vexed when he heard of the honor done to Sir Tristram, and the stranger having departed, he said to his two knights:

"Now will I tell you my counsel, because ye are the men whom I most trust to. I would have you know that my coming hither is to this intent—to destroy Sir Tristram by wiles or by treachery; and it shall go hard if ever he escape our hands."

"Alas," said Sir Bersules, "what mean you? If you are set on such a plan, you are shamefully disposed. For Sir Tristram is the knight of most worship whom we know living; I warn you plainly, I will never consent to do him death; and therefore I will yield my service and forsake you."

When King Mark heard him speak thus, suddenly he drew his sword, and saying, "A traitor!" smote Sir Bersules on the head, so that the sword went through to his teeth.

Amant the knight and Mark's squires, when they saw him do that villainous deed, said, "It was foul done and mischievously; wherefore we will do thee no more service, and wit thou well, we will appeach thee of murder before King Arthur."

King Mark was wonderly wroth at these bold words, and would have slain Amant also, but he and the two squires held together, and set his malice at nought. Seeing he could not be revenged on them, King Mark said to the knight Amant:

"Wit thou well, if thou accuse me of murder, I shall defend myself before King Arthur; but I require thee that thou tell not my name, that I am King Mark, whatsoever come of me."

"As for that," said Sir Amant, "I will not reveal your name."

Thus they parted, and Amant and his companions took the body of Bersules and buried it.

King Mark rode till he came to a fountain, and there he rested himself, and stood in doubt whether he would ride to Arthur's Court or not, or return again to his own country. As he thus rested by the fountain there came by him a knight well armed, on horseback, and he alighted, and tying his horse to a tree, he sat him down by the brink of the fountain, and there made the dolefullest complaint of unhappy love that ever man heard; and all this while he was not aware of King Mark.

Then King Mark arose, and went near him, and said:

"Fair knight, ye have made a piteous complaint."

"Truly," said the knight, "it is a hundredfold more rueful than my heart can utter."

"I require you," said King Mark; "tell me your name."

"Sir," said he, "as for my name, I will not hide it from any knight who beareth a shield; my name is Sir Lamorak of Wales."

But when he heard King Mark speak, the stranger knight knew well by his speech that he was from Cornwall.

"Sir," said Sir Lamorak, "I understand by your tongue ye be of Cornwall, wherein there dwelleth the shamefullest king now living, for he is a great enemy of all good knights; and that is well proved, for he hath chased out of that country Sir Tristram, who is the most renowned knight now alive, and all knights speak honor of him; and for jealousy King Mark hath chased him out of his country. It is a pity," added Sir Lamorak, "that such a false knight-coward as King Mark should be matched with such a fair and good lady as La Belle Iseult; for all the world speaketh shame of him, and of her all the praise that any Queen can have."

"I have nothing to do in the matter," said King Mark; "neither will I speak anything thereof."

"Well spoken," said Sir Lamorak.

"Sir, can ye tell me any tidings?"

"I can tell you," said Sir Lamorak, "that there is speedily to be a great tournament beside Camelot, at the Castle of Jagent. The King with the Hundred Knights, and the King of Ireland, have, I believe, appointed the tournament."

Just then up came a knight, who saluted them both; this was Sir Dinadan, who had formerly journeyed with Sir Tristram; when he found one of them was a knight of Cornwall, he spoke worse things of King Mark a thousandfold than Sir Lamorak had done.

Presently he offered to joust with King Mark, but the King was full loath; however, he urged him so that at last the King jousted with Sir Lamorak, and the latter overthrew him twice. Sir Lamorak seeing how he fared, said, "Sir Knight, what cheer? It seems to me you have nearly had your fill of fighting. It were pity to do you any more harm, for you are but a mean knight, therefore I give you leave to go where you list."

"Thanks," said King Mark, "for you and I are not equally matched."

Then Sir Dinadan mocked King Mark, and said:

"You are not able to match a good knight."

"As for that," said King Mark, "the first time I jousted with this knight, ye refused him."

"Think you it is a shame to me?" said Sir Dinadan. "Nay, sir, it is ever honor to a knight to refuse that thing which he cannot attain to. Therefore it would have been much more to your honor to have refused him as I did. For I warn you plainly he is able to beat five such as you and I, for ye knights of Cornwall are no men of worship, as other knights are. And because you are no men of worship, you hate all men of worship; for never was bred in your country such a knight as Sir Tristram."

A FALSE KNIGHT-COWARD

AFTER this they all rode forth together, King Mark, Sir Lamorak, and Sir Dinadan, till they came to a bridge, at the end of which stood a fair tower. When they reached this they begged for a lodging.

"Ye are right welcome," said the knights of the Castle, "for the sake of the lord of this Castle, who is called Sir Tor."

They were led into a fair court, well repaired, and they had passing good cheer till the lieutenant of the Castle, who was called Berluse, espied King Mark of Cornwall.

Then said Berluse, "Sir Knight, I know you better than you ween, for you are King Mark, who slew my father before my own eyes, and me ye would have slain, had I not escaped into a wood. Nevertheless, for the love of the lord of this Castle, I will neither hurt you nor harm you, nor any of your fellowship, as long as you are here. But understand, when you are past this lodging, I shall hurt you if I can, for you slew my father treacherously. But first for the love of my lord, Sir Tor, and then for love of Sir Lamorak the honorable knight who is here also, you shall have no ill lodging. It is a pity you should ever be in the company of good knights, for you are the most villainous knight or King now known to be alive. For you are a destroyer of good knights, and all that you do is but treachery."

King Mark was sorely ashamed and said but little in answer. But when Sir Lamorak and Sir Dinadan knew he was King Mark they were sorry to have his companionship.

On the morrow they arose early, and King Mark and Sir Dinadan rode together. Three miles from their lodging three knights met them; Sir Berluse was one, and the others his two cousins. Sir Berluse saw King Mark, and cried out loud:

Traitor, keep thee from me, for wit thou well, I am Berluse."

"Sir Knight," said Sir Dinadan, "I counsel you to leave off at present, for he is riding to King Arthur; and because I have promised to conduct him to my lord King Arthur, I must needs take part with him, although I do not love his character, and fain would be away from him."

"Well, Dinadan," said Sir Berluse, "I am sorry that you will take part with him, but now do your best!" Thereupon he hurtled to King Mark, and smote him sore upon the shield, so that he bore him clean out of his saddle to the earth.

Dinadan, seeing this, ran to help the King, and there began a great battle, for Berluse and his companions held together strongly. Through the great strength of Sir Dinadan, King Mark threw Berluse to the ground, and his two cousins fled; if it had not been for Sir Dinadan, King Mark would have slain Sir Berluse; Sir Dinadan rescued his life, for King Mark was nothing but a murderer.

Then King Mark and Sir Dinadan took their horses and departed, leaving Sir Berluse behind sore wounded.

About four leagues further on they came to a bridge, where hovered a knight on horseback, armed and ready to joust. It was the custom that none should pass the bridge unless he jousted with this knight. King Mark would by no means joust, therefore Sir Dinadan could in no manner refuse. He was smitten at once to the earth, but when he challenged his adversary to continue the battle on foot with swords, the stranger knight would not fight any more, saying it was not the custom of the bridge. Sir Dinadan was passing wroth that he could not be revenged on the knight, but there was no help for it.

As they rode on their way King Mark began to mock Sir Dinadan, saying:

"I thought you Knights of the Round Table could in no wise find your match!"

"You say well," said Dinadan, "as for your Cornish folk, on my life, I call you none of the best knights; but since you have such scorn of me, I challenge you to joust with me, to prove my strength."

"Not so," said King Mark, "for I will not fight with you on any account. But I require of you one thing, that when you come to Arthur's Castle, do not reveal my name, for I am so hated there."

"It is shame to you," said Sir Dinadan, "that you govern yourself so disgracefully, for I see you are full of cowardice, and you are a murderer, and that is the greatest shame that a knight can have; for never a knight being a murderer can have honor, nor ever shall have. For I saw lately that except for my help, you would have slain Sir Berluse, a better knight than you are, or ever will be, and one of more prowess."

As they thus talked, they saw riding towards them over a plain, six knights of the Court of King Arthur, well armed at all points. By their shields Sir Dinadan knew them well. The first was the good knight Sir Uwaine, son of King Uriens; the second was the noble knight Sir Brandiles; the third was Ozana, "Hardy-Heart"; the fourth was Uwaine the Adventurous; the fifth was Sir Agrivaine, the sixth Sir Mordred, brother to Sir Gawaine, and son to King Lot's wife, of Orkney.

When Sir Dinadan saw these six knights, he thought to himself he would bring King Mark by some wile to joust with one of them. They followed them three good English miles, and then King Mark was aware where they all six sat near a well, eating and drinking such food as they had, their horses walking about, or tied near, and their shields hung around in diverse places.

"Lo," said Sir Dinadan, "yonder are knights-errant, who will joust with us."

"Heaven forbid," said King Mark, "for they are six, and we are but two."

"As for that," said Sir Dinadan, "let us not spare, for I will assay the foremost." And therewith he made him ready.

No sooner did King Mark see him do so, than as fast as Sir Dinadan rode towards the knights, King Mark rode away from them, with all his menial company.

Directly Sir Dinadan saw King Mark was gone, he set the spear out of the rest, and threw his shield behind his back, and came riding to the fellowship of the Round Table. And Sir Uwaine at once knew Sir Dinadan, and welcomed him, and so did all his companions.

CHASED BY THE KING'S FOOL

THEN the six knights asked Sir Dinadan about his adventures, and whether he had seen Sir Tristram or Sir Lancelot.

"Truly," said Sir Dinadan, "I have seen nothing of them since I left Camelot."

"What knight is that," said Sir Brandiles, "who so suddenly departed from you, and rode over yonder field?"

"Sir," said he, "it was a knight of Cornwall, and the most horrible coward that ever bestrode horse."

Having rested themselves and spoken together they took their horses, and rode to a castle where dwelt an old knight who received all knights-errant with hearty good cheer. Here also arrived another knight, Sir Griflet, who was made welcome.

As Sir Dinadan walked about and looked over the castle he came across a chamber in which he espied King Mark; then he rebuked him, and asked why he had departed in that cowardly fashion.

"Because I durst not abide," he said, "for the knights were so many. But how did you escape?"

"They were better friends than I thought they had been," said Dinadan.

"Who is captain of that fellowship?" asked the King.

To frighten him, Dinadan answered that it was Sir Lancelot of the Lake.

"Oh," said the King, "can I know Sir Lancelot by his shield?"

"Yes," answered Dinadan, "for he beareth a shield of silver and black bars." All this he said to frighten the King, for Sir Lancelot was not in that fellowship.

"Now I pray you," said King Mark, "that you will ride in my company."

"I am not willing to do that," said Dinadan, "because you forsook my company," and he at once left King Mark, and went to his own companions.

Mounting their horses, they rode on their way, and talked of the Cornish knight, for Dinadan told them he was in the castle where they were lodged.

"Well said," spoke Sir Griflet, "for here I have brought Sir Dagonet, King Arthur's fool, the best fellow and the merriest in the world."

"Would you like a jest?" said Sir Dinadan. "I told the Cornish knight that Sir Lancelot is here, and he asked me what shield he bore. I answered that he bore the same shield which Sir Mordred beareth."

"I am hurt, and cannot well bear my shield and armor," said Sir Mordred, "therefore put them on Sir Dagonet, and let him assail the Cornish knight."

"That shall be done, by my faith," said Sir Dagonet.

Then Dagonet was quickly arrayed in Mordred's armor, and he was set on a great horse, with a spear in his hand.

"Now," said Dagonet, "show me the knight, and I trow I shall bear him down."

So they all rode to the side of the wood, and waited there till King Mark came by that way. Then they put forth Sir Dagonet, and he went straight at King Mark. When he came near he cried as if he were mad:

"Keep thee, knight of Cornwall, for I will slay thee!"

As soon as King Mark saw his shield he said to himself,

"Yonder is Sir Lancelot; alas, now am I destroyed!" Therewith he made his horse gallop away as fast as it could, through thick and thin, while Sir Dagonet followed, calling out and rating him like a madman through the great forest.

When all the other knights saw Sir Dagonet thus chase King Mark they laughed as if they would never stop, and taking their horses, they rode after to see how Sir Dagonet sped, for they would not on any account have the jester hurt; for King Arthur loved him passing well, and had made him knight with his own hands; and at every tournament Dagonet was present and made Arthur laugh at his drollery. Thus the knights rode here and there, chasing after King Mark, so that all the forest rang with the noise.

As King Mark fled, he came by chance near a well, where stood a knight-errant on horseback, armed at all points, with a great spear in his hand. When he saw King Mark come flying, he said:

"Knight, return again for shame, and stand with me, and I shall be thy warrant."

"Ah, fair knight," said King Mark, "let me pass, for yonder cometh after me the best knight in the world, with the black barred shield."

"Fie for shame," said the knight, "he is none of the worthy knights. And if he were Sir Lancelot or Sir Tristram, I should not fear to meet the better of them both."

King Mark hearing him speak with such valor, turned his horse, and waited beside him.

Then that strong knight levelled his spear against Dagonet, and smote him so sore that he bore him over his horse's tail, and nearly broke his neck. The knights of King Arthur's Court were very angry when they saw Dagonet have that fall, and each in turn challenged the stranger knight, but one after another he overthrew them all, except Sir Mordred, who was unarmed, and Sir Dinadan, who was some way behind. And this being done, the strong knight rode slowly on his way, and King Mark after his, praising him very much; but he would answer nothing, only sighed wonderly sore, hanging down his head, and taking no heed of his companion's words.

After riding about three English miles, the stranger knight called to him a varlet, one of King Mark's servants, and bade him—"Ride to yonder fair manor, and commend me to the lady of the castle, and pray her to send me refreshment of good meat and drink. And if she ask thee what I am, tell her that I am the knight that follows the Questing Beast."

The varlet went his way, and coming to the manor, he saluted the lady, and told her from whence he came. And when she understood he had been sent by the knight that followed the Questing Beast,—"Oh," she cried, "when shall I see that noble knight, my dear son, Palamides? Alas, will he not abide with me?" And therewith she wept for sorrow, and gave the varlet all that he asked as quickly as she could.

As soon as the varlet returned to King Mark and the other knight, he told his master secretly that the stranger's name was Sir Palamides.

"I am well pleased," said King Mark, "but hold thee still, and say nothing."

Then they alighted, and sat down to rest awhile, and very soon King Mark fell asleep.

When Sir Palamides found him sound asleep, he took his horse and rode his way. "I will not be in the company of a sleeping knight," he said, and he rode off at a great pace.

KING FOX AT CAMELOT

By and by King Mark awoke, and finding Sir Palamides gone, he rode after him, and sought him through the forest. Sir Dinadan, who was much vexed at the way the other knights of his party had sped, also rode in search of him. Late in the evening he heard a doleful noise, as of a man lamenting; when he came near, he alighted, and went towards it on foot, and then he was aware of a knight who stood under a tree, his horse tied beside him, and the helm off his head. The knight kept up always a doleful complaint, and it was about La Belle Iseult, the Queen of Cornwall.

Long ago, before her marriage, when she was a Princess in Ireland the brave pagan knight Sir Palamides had loved the beautiful Iseult. He had never forgotten her, and still mourned bitterly because she did not return his love.

"Ah, fair lady," he was saying now, "why do I love thee? Thou are fairest of all others, yet never didst thou show love to me, nor kindness. Alas, yet I cannot help but love thee! And I may not blame thee, fair lady, for mine eyes are the cause of this sorrow. The falsest King and knight is your husband, and the most coward and full of treachery is your lord, King Mark. Alas, that ever so fair a lady, and peerless above all others should be matched with the most villainous knight of the world!"

In the meanwhile King Mark also had drawn near, and all this language that Sir Palamides said of him, he heard. Therefore he was much frightened when he saw Sir Dinadan, lest if he espied him, he would tell Sir Palamides that he was King Mark. Accordingly he withdrew, and went back to his servants where he had told them to wait, and rode on as fast as he could to Camelot.

There on the same day he found Sir Amant ready, who had accused him before King Arthur of the murder of his companion knight, Sir Bersules. As was the custom of those times, the King commanded them to do battle, and by misadventure King Mark smote Amant through the body. And yet Amant's was the righteous quarrel.

King Mark immediately took his horse, and left the Court, dreading that Sir Dinadan would tell Sir Tristram and Sir Palamides who he was.

There were some of Queen Iseult's maidens at Camelot, who knew Sir Amant well, and by leave of King Arthur they went and spoke to him while he lay sore wounded.

"Ah, fair damsels," he said, "commend me to La Belle Iseult, and tell her that I am slain for the love of her and Sir Tristram." And there he told the damsels how in cowardly fashion King Mark had slain him and Sir Bersules, his companion. "For that deed I appeached him of murder, and here I am slain in a righteous quarrel; and all this because Sir Bersules and I would not consent by treachery to slay the noble knight Sir Tristram."

The news was quickly borne to the King and Queen, and to all the lords and ladies, that it was King Mark who had slain Sir Amant, and Sir Bersules beforehand, which was the reason why Amant had fought with him. King Arthur was wroth out of measure, and so were all the other knights.

But when Sir Tristram knew all the matter, he made great dole, and wept for sorrow for the loss of the two noble knights Sir Bersules and Sir Amant.

Sir Lancelot seeing Sir Tristram weep went hastily to King Arthur, and said, "Sir, I pray you, give me leave to go after yonder false King and knight."

"I pray you, fetch him again," said King Arthur, "but I would not that you slew him, for my honor."

Then Sir Lancelot armed in all haste, and mounted upon a great horse, and taking a spear in his hand, rode after King Mark. And within three English miles Sir Lancelot overtook him.

"Turn, recreant King and knight!" he cried; "for whether thou wilt, or not, thou shalt go with me to King Arthur's Court."

King Mark turned back, and looked at Sir Lancelot. "Fair Sir," he said, "what is your name?"

"Wit thou my name is Sir Lancelot, and therefore, defend thee!"

When King Mark knew that it was Sir Lancelot, and that he was coming fast upon him with a spear, he cried aloud, "I yield myself to thee, Sir Lancelot, honorable knight!"

But Sir Lancelot would not hear him, but came fast upon him. King Mark seeing this, made no defense, but tumbled down out of the saddle to the earth like a sack, and there he lay still, and cried mercy of Sir Lancelot.

"Arise, recreant knight and King!"

"I will not fight," said King Mark, "but I will go with you wherever you like."

"Alas, alas, that I may not give thee one buffet," said Sir Lancelot, "for the love of Sir Tristram and La Belle Iseult, and for the two knights who thou hast slain treacherously."

But he would not disobey King Arthur's command, so he brought the traitor back unhurt to Camelot. There King Mark alighted in great haste, and threw his helm and his sword from him on the earth, and falling flat on the ground at King Arthur's feet, he put himself into his grace and mercy.

"Truly," said King Arthur, "in a manner ye are welcome, and in a manner ye are not welcome. In this manner ye are welcome, that ye come hither in spite of yourself, I suppose?"

"That is truth," said King Mark, "or else I had not been here: for my lord Sir Lancelot brought me hither through his might, and to him I have yielded myself as recreant."

"Well," said King Arthur, "you understand you ought to do me service, homage, and fealty, and never would you do me any, but always you have been against me, and a destroyer of my knights. Now, how will you acquit you?"

"Sir," said King Mark, "exactly as your lordship will require me, I will make large amends, to the ultmost in my power." For he was always a fair speaker, and false underneath.

Then because of his pleasure in Sir Tristram, and in order to make the two reconciled, and to do a good turn to Tristram, King Arthur kept King Mark for a while at Camelot. And one day he said to him, "Sir, I pray you to give me a gift that I shall ask you."

"Sir," said King Mark, "I will give you whatsoever you desire, if it be in my power."

"Thanks," said King Arthur, "this I will ask you, that you will be a good lord to Sir Tristram, for he is a man of great honor; and that you will take him with you into Cornwall, and let him see his friends, and there cherish him for my sake."

"Sir," said King Mark, "I promise you by the faith of my body, and by the faith I owe to God and to you, I will honor him, for your sake, in all that I can or may."

"And I will forgive all the evil that ever I owed you," said King Arthur, "if so be you will swear that on a book before me."

"Willingly," said King Mark.

So there he swore upon a book before King Arthur and all his knights, and King Mark and Sir Tristram took each other by the hands hard knit together in token of friendship.

But for all that, King Mark was false in thought, as it proved afterwards, for as soon as the chance came he threw Sir Tristram into prison, and would cowardly have slain him.

"BEWARE, I COUNSEL THEE,
OF TREACHERY!"

SOON after this, King Mark took his leave to go back to Cornwall, and Sir Tristram made ready to ride with him, wherefore most of the Knights of the Round Table were sad and angry; and in especial Sir Lancelot, Sir Lamorak, and Sir Dinadan were wroth out of measure. For well they knew King Mark would slay or destroy Sir Tristram. And Sir Tristram himself was almost dazed with sorrow to leave the noble fellowship of the Round Table.

"Alas," said Sir Lancelot to King Arthur, "what have you done? For you will lose the man of most worship that ever came into your Court."

"It was his own desire," said Arthur, "and therefore I could not help it. For I have done all that I can, and made King Mark and Sir Tristram agreed."

"Agreed!" said Sir Lancelot. "Fie on that agreement, for you shall hear that King Mark will slay Sir Tristram, or put him in prison, for he is the most coward and villainous King and knight now living."

Sir Lancelot thereupon went to King Mark.

"Sir King," he said, "wit thou well, the good knight Sir Tristram shall go with thee. But beware, I counsel thee, of treachery; for if thou do mischief to that knight, by any manner of falsehood or treason, by the faith I owe to God, and to the order of knighthood, I shall slay thee with mine own hands."

"Sir Lancelot," said the King, "you say too much to me; I have said and sworn amply before King Arthur, in hearing of all his knights, that I shall not slay nor betray Sir Tristram. It were overmuch shame to me to break my promise."

"You say well," said Sir Lancelot, "but you are called so false and full of treason that no man can believe you. Forsooth, it is well known wherefore you came into this country —for none other cause than to slay Sir Tristram."

So with great dole King Mark and Sir Tristram rode away together. It was Sir Tristram's own will and wish to go back to Cornwall, and all was for the sake of seeing La Belle Iseult again; for Sir Tristram felt he could endure no longer without a sight of her.

By and by there came to Camelot a knight out of Cornwall, Sir Fergus, a fellow of the Round Table, and he told good tidings of Sir Tristram, and how he had left him in the Castle of Tintagel. Afterwards came a damsel, a maiden of Sir Tristram's, who brought goodly letters to King Arthur and Sir Lancelot, and she was made very welcome by the King, and the Queen Guinevere, and Sir Lancelot. And they wrote goodly letters back again. But Sir Lancelot ever bade Sir Tristram beware of King Mark, for he always called him in his letters "King Fox," as one who saith, "He fareth all with wiles and treason." Sir Tristram was grateful to Lancelot in his heart for this caution.

The damsel took King Arthur's and Sir Lancelot's letters to La Belle Iseult, whereat she was in great joy.

"Fair damsel," said La Belle Iseult, "how fareth my lord Arthur, and the Queen Guinevere, and the noble knight, Sir Lancelot of the Lake?"

She answered to make a short tale, "Much the better because you and Sir Tristram are in joy."

"Truly," said La Belle Iseult, "Sir Tristram suffereth great pain for me, and I for him."

The damsel had also brought back letters to King Mark

from Camelot. When he had read and understood them, he was wroth with Sir Tristram, for he reflected that he had sent the damsel to King Arthur; because Arthur and Lancelot in a manner threatened King Mark in these letters. And as King Mark read them, he plotted treachery to Sir Tristram.

"Damsel," said King Mark, "will you ride again, and bear letters from me to King Arthur?"

"Sir," she said, "I will be at your command, to ride when you will."

"Well spoken," said the King. "Come again tomorrow, and fetch your letters."

But on the morrow when the damsel went to King Mark, to fetch the letters, the King told her he did not intend just then to send any. Privily, however, he had letters written which he sent secretly to King Arthur, and Queen Guinevere, and Sir Lancelot.

His varlet found the King and Queen in Wales, at Carleon. He arrived while they were in church, and when the service was over, and they were by themselves, they opened their letters.

The beginning of King Mark's letter spoke abruptly to King Arthur, and bade him meddle with his own affairs, and with his wife, and with his knights, for he had enough to do to rule, and to look after his wife.

When King Arthur understood the letter he mused of many things, and thought of his sister's words, Queen Morgan le Fay, and how she had said wicked things of Queen Guinevere, and of Sir Lancelot. And over this thought he pondered a great while. Then he bethought him again how his sister had always been his enemy, and that she hated the Queen, and Sir Lancelot, and so he put all that out of his mind. Then King Arthur read the letter again, and the latter clause said that King Mark took Sir Tristram for his mortal enemy, whereby he put Arthur out of doubt that he would be revenged on Sir Tristram. And at this King Arthur was wroth with King Mark.

When Queen Guinevere read her letter and understood it, she was angry beyond measure, for it spoke shamefully of her, and of Sir Lancelot. She sent the letter to Sir Lancelot, whom it also enraged.

"Sir," said Dinadan, "wherefore are you angry? Reveal your heart to me. For truly you know well I owe you goodwill, howbeit I am a poor knight, and a servitor to you, and to all good knights. For though I am not of worship myself, yet I love all those that are of worship."

"It is true," said Sir Lancelot, "and because you are a trusty knight, I will tell you what is the matter."

When Dinadan had read all the shameful letters, he said, "This is my counsel; set you nought by these threats, for King Mark is so villainous, that no man will ever get at him by fair speech. But you shall see what I will do. I will make a song about him, and it shall be known in all countries, and I shall send a harper to sing it before King Mark himself."

So Sir Dinadan went at once and made a song, telling about King Mark, and all the false and cowardly deeds that he was forever doing. In this way he hoped to bring the crafty King to shame and disgrace. He taught the song to a harper called Eliot, who afterwards taught it to many other harpers. By permission of King Arthur and Sir Lancelot, these harpers went straight into Wales, and into Cornwall, to sing this lay which Sir Dinadan had made—which was the worst lay that ever harper sang with harp, or with any other instrument.

THE SIEGE OF TINTAGEL CASTLE

WHILE Sir Tristram was at King Mark's Court it happened he got sorely hurt in a tournament, and to rest himself he went to stay in a Castle with a good knight, Sir Dinas, the Steward. Then from the Saxon land came a great number of men at arms, with a hideous host, and they landed in Cornwall near the Castle of Tintagel. Their captain's name was Elias, a good man of arms.

When King Mark learned that his enemies were entered into his land, he made great dole, for he by no means wished to send for Sir Tristram, because of his deadly hatred to him. But his counsel, foreseeing the many perils from the strength of the enemy, declared that King Mark must send for Sir Tristram, or else the Saxons would never be overcome.

"Well," said King Mark, "I will act on your counsel," but he was still very loath to do so.

When Sir Tristram was come the King said thus: "Fair nephew, Sir Tristram, this is all: here are come our enemies of Saxony, who are now nigh at hand. Without tarrying they must be met with at once, or else they will destroy this land."

Tristram replied that he was at the King's command, but that for eight days he could bear no arms, for his wounds were not yet whole. The King told him to go back and rest for eight days, and in the meanwhile he would go and meet the Saxons with all his power.

So King Mark collected a great army, and by advice of his knights issued out of the Castle of Tintagel against his enemies. Long endured the battle, and many were slain, but at the last King Mark was forced to withdraw to the Castle, with great slaughter of his people. The Saxons followed on so fast that ten of them got within the gates, and four were slain at the fall of the portcullis.

Therewith came Elias, and bade King Mark yield up the Castle, for he would not be able to hold it any time. The King replied that he would yield up the Castle if he were not soon rescued, then he sent quickly again to Sir Tristram.

By this time Tristram was well, and he had got ten good knights of Arthur's, and with them he rode to Tintagel. When he saw the great host of Saxons, he marvelled greatly. He rode by the woods and the ditches as secretly as he could till he came near the gates, and then he and his knights fought their way through the Saxons who opposed them, and so they entered into the Castle of Tintagel.

King Mark was rejoiced at his coming and so were all his company.

On the morrow Elias the captain sent a message to King Mark, bidding him come out and do battle.

"For now the good knight Sir Tristram has joined thee," he said, "it will be shame to thee to keep within thy walls."

King Mark was wroth at this, and spoke no word, but went to Sir Tristram, and asked him his counsel. Sir Tristram asked if he might send the answer to Elias. Willingly, the King replied. So Sir Tristram spoke thus to the messenger:

"Bear thy lord word from the King and me that we will do battle with him tomorrow in the open field."

"What is your name?" said the messenger.

"Wit thou well, my name is Sir Tristram of Lyonesse."

Therewith the messenger departed, and told his lord Elias all that he had heard.

By consent of King Mark, Sir Tristram took command of the army, and that same night he burnt all the Saxon ships to the water's edge. As soon as Elias heard the news, he said: "That was of Sir Tristram's doing, for he reckoneth that we shall never escape, any mother's son of us; therefore, fair fellows, fight freely tomorrow, and discomfort yourself nought for any knight, though he be the best knight in the world; he cannot fight against all of us at once."

So the leaders of the two armies arranged their men, and those who were within the Casttle of Tintagel issued forth, and those that were outside set fiercely upon them, and great deeds of valor were done on either side. Thus they fought till it was night, when because of the great slaughter, and of the wounded people, both parties withdrew to their rest.

When King Mark returned within the Castle of Tintagel he lacked of his knights a hundred; and the Saxons outside lacked two hundred. Then councils were held, and both parties were loath to fight again, if they could escape with honor.

Elias the captain made great dole when he learned of the death of his men, and he was wroth out of measure when he found the others were unwilling to go to battle again. He sent word to King Mark, asking whether he would find a knight who would fight for him, man against man; and that if he could slay King Mark's champion, he was to have tribute from Cornwall yearly; and if King Mark's knight slew the Saxon champion, Elias was to release his claim forever.

On receipt of this message King Mark called all his Barons together, to know what was best to be done. They all said at once they had no desire to fight any more in the field, for if it had not been for Sir Tristram's prowess, they would most likely never have escaped. Therefore they thought it would be well to find a champion that would do battle with Elias, for it was a knightly offer.

But when all this was said, they could find no knight who would do battle.

"Alas," said King Mark, "then am I utterly shamed, and utterly destroyed, unless my nephew Sir Tristram will take the battle upon him."

"Wit you well," said they all, "he had yesterday overmuch on hand, and he is weary for travail, and sore wounded."

"Where is he?" said King Mark.

"Sir," said they, "he is in his bed, to repose himself."

"Alas," said King Mark, "unless I have the succor of my nephew Sir Tristram I am utterly destroyed for ever."

One of the Barons, accordingly, went to Sir Tristram where he lay, and told him what King Mark had said. Sir Tristram arose quickly, and, putting on a long gown, came before the King and all the lords. And when he saw them all so dismayed he asked the King and the lords what tidings were with them.

"Never worse," said the King; and he told him the message that Elias had sent.

Then Tristram said that since King Mark needed his succor he would do all that lay in his power, although he was sore bruised and hurt; therefore the Saxon messenger should carry back word to Elias that Sir Tristram, King Arthur's knight, and Knight of the Round Table, would tomorrow meet with him on horseback, to do battle as long as his horse could endure, and after that to do battle on foot to the death.

Hostage was given on both sides, and it was made as sure as it could be that whichever party had the victory, so the matter was to end. Both hosts were then assembled on the field outside the Castle of Tintagel, and no one was armed but Sir Tristram and Sir Elias.

For the space of nearly an hour they fought with the uttermost fury, wounding each other sorely; by that time Sir Tristram waxed very faint for want of blood, and began to retreat. Sir Elias, seeing this, followed fiercely on him, and wounded him in many places. Sir Tristram wavered here and there, and covered himself weakly with his shield, so that all men said he was overcome, for Sir Elias had given him twenty strokes against one. At this there was laughing of the Saxon party, and great grief on King Mark's side.

"Alas!" said the King, "we are ashamed and destroyed for ever."

Thus, as they stood and beheld both parties, the one laughing, and the other weeping, Sir Tristram remembered him of his lady, La Belle Iseult, and how he was likely never to come again into her presence. Then he pulled up his shield, which had hung full low, and attacked Elias with such fury that he completely shattered his shield and hauberk.

Now it was King Mark who began to laugh, and all the Cornish men, and the Saxons to weep. And Sir Tristram kept saying to Elias, "Yield thee!" And when he saw him so staggering on the ground, he said, "Sir Elias, I am right sorry for thee, for thou art a passing good knight, as ever I met withal, except Sir Lancelot."

Therewith Sir Elias fell to the earth, and died.

239

"FALSE HAST THOU EVER BEEN; SO WILT THOU END!"

KING Mark made a great feast for joy because the Saxons were driven out of his country, yet for all this he would gladly have slain Sir Tristram. To the feast came Eliot the harper, with the song Sir Dinadan had made; and because he was a cunning harper men heard him sing that same song, which spoke most villainously of King Mark's treachery, as ever man heard.

When the harper had sung his song to the end, King Mark was wonderfully wroth.

"Thou harper," he said, "how darest thou be so bold as to sing this song before me?"

"Sir," said Eliot, "wit you well, I am a minstrel, and I must do as I am commanded by those lords whose arms I bear. Sir Dinadan, a Knight of the Round Table, made this song, and bade me sing it before you."

"Thou sayest well," said King Mark, "and because thou art a minstrel, thou shalt go free, but I charge thee, hie thee fast out of my sight."

So the harper departed, and went to Sir Tristram, and told him how he had sped. Then Tristram had goodly letters written to Lancelot and Sir Dinadan, and had the harper conducted safely out of the country.

But to say that King Mark was wonderfully wroth, is only the truth, for he deemed that the lay which was sung before him was made by Sir Tristram's counsel; he therefore resolved to slay him and all his well-wishers in that country, and immediately began to plot treachery against him.

A great tournament and jousts had been proclaimed in the coasts of Cornwall; and this had been done by Sir Galahalt, the high prince, and King Bagdemagus, with the intent to slay Sir Lancelot, or else to shame him utterly. For Sir Lancelot always won the highest prize, therefore this prince and this King made these jousts against him, meaning both to set upon him at once, with all their knights.

Their purpose was revealed to King Mark, at which he was very glad. He determined that he would have Sir Tristram at that tournament, disguised so that no man should know him, intending that the high prince should think he was Sir Lancelot.

Sir Tristram accordingly came to these jousts. Sir Lancelot at that moment was not there, but when the people saw a disguised knight do such deeds of arms, they thought it must be Sir Lancelot, and in especial, King Mark said plainly it was Sir Lancelot. Then they set upon him, both King Bagdemagus, and the high prince, and their knights, so that it was a wonder that ever Sir Tristram could withstand such an attack.

But notwithstanding all he had to endure, Sir Tristram won the prize at the tournament, and there he hurt many knights, and bruised them, although they, too, hurt and bruised him sorely.

When the jousts were all done the knights knew well it was Tristram of Lyonesse. Those of King Mark's party were glad that Sir Tristram was hurt; but the other knights were sorry, for Sir Tristram was not so hated from envy as was Sir Lancelot within the realm of England.

Then came King Mark to Sir Tristram, and said:

"Fair nephew, I am sorry for your hurts."

"Thanks, my lord," said Sir Tristram.

King Mark made Sir Tristram to be put in a horse-bier, in great sign of love, and he said: "Fair cousin, I shall be your physician myself."

So he rode forth with Sir Tristram, and brought him to a Castle, by daylight. There he made him eat, and afterwards he gave him a drink, which as soon as he had swallowed, made him fall asleep.

When it was night King Mark had him carried to another Castle, and there he put him into a strong prison, and appointed a man and a woman to give him food and drink.

And there Sir Tristram remained a long while.

By and by Sir Tristram was missed, but no one knew what had become of him. At last Queen Iseult went quietly to a knight called Sir Sadok, and begged him to seek out where he was. Finding that he had been treacherously flung into prison, Sir Sadok went to the good knight Sir Dinas, the Steward, and told him of all King Mark's treason and felony. Then Sir Dinas defied such a King, and said he would give up his lands which he held of him, and all manner of knights said the same thing. By the advice of Sir Sadok and Sir Dinas they fortified all the towns and castles within the country of Lyonesse, and assembled all the people they could collect.

King Mark heard how Sir Sadok and Sir Dinas were risen in the country of Lyonesse, and afraid lest he should lose his kingdom, he at once began to concoct fresh wiles and stratagems. This was what he did. He caused counterfeit letters to be written from the Pope, and made a strange clerk bear them to himself; and these letters specified that King Mark should make ready with his army to come to the Pope, to help to go to Jerusalem, to make war upon the Saracens. When the clerk arrived, King Mark sent him with these letters to Sir Tristram, and bade him say thus: That if he would go to war against the miscreants, he should be let out of prison, and restored to all his power. For King Mark now wanted an excuse to set Sir Tristram free.

When Sir Tristram understood this letter, he said to the clerk:

"Ah, King Mark, ever hast thou been a traitor, and ever will be! But, clerk, say thou thus unto King Mark: Since the Pope hath sent for him, bid him go thither himself, for tell him, traitor King as he is, I will not go at his command, get I out of my prison as I may. For I see I am well rewarded for my true service!"

The clerk returned to King Mark, and told him of Sir Tristram's answer.

"Well," said King Mark, "yet shall he be beguiled."

So he went into his chamber and counterfeited other letters, and these specified that the Pope desired Sir Tristram to come himself to make war upon the miscreants. The clerk went again to Sir Tristram, and took him these letters, but when he beheld them, he quickly espied they were of King Mark's forging, and was on his guard not to fall into any trap the King might have set for him.

"Ah," said Sir Tristram, "false hast thou ever been, King Mark, and so wilt thou end."

By that time four knights, who had been wounded in a skirmish between King Mark's men and Sir Sadok's, reached the Castle of Tintagel. Directly they saw King Mark they cried, "King, why dost thou not flee, for all this country is clearly arisen against thee!" which made the King very angry indeed.

In the meanwhile there came into the country Sir Percival of Wales to seek Sir Tristram, and hearing he was in prison, he speedily by his knightly power delivered him. Then he rode straight to King Mark and told him how he had rescued Sir Tristram. Also he told the King he had done himself great shame by putting Tristram into prison, for he was the knight of most renown then living in all the world.

Sir Percival could not tarry in Cornwall, for he was obliged to go into Wales. As soon he he had departed King Mark bethought himself of more treachery, although he had promised Sir Percival never, by any means to hurt Sir Tristram. He sent word at once to Sir Dinas, to put down all the people he had raised, for he said on oath that he was going himself to the Pope of Rome, to do battle against the Saracens,—and that was a fairer war than thus to raise the people against their King.

Sir Dinas, believing what King Mark said, in all haste dismissed the people, and every man departed to his own home. This was just what King Mark had hoped for. No sooner were they gone than, in spite of his promise to Sir Percival, he had Tristram once more seized by treachery.

When Queen Iseult knew that Sir Tristram was again in prison she was as full of sorrow as any lady could be. But Sir Tristram managed to get a letter sent to her, in which he said that if she would have a vessel made ready, he would go with her to the realm of England, where Arthur was King, and thus they would escape the cruelty and treachery of King Mark. He knew by this time that it was useless to trust any longer to fair words or promises, and that the only hope of safety for himself and Queen Iseult was to leave Cornwall forever. La Belle Iseult at once sent back an answer, bidding Sir Tristram be of good comfort, for she would have the vessel made ready, and everything to carry out their purpose.

Then she sent to Sir Dinas, the Steward, and to Sir Sadok, praying them by any means to take King Mark and keep him prisoner until the time when she and Sir Tristram had departed to the realm of England. Knowing King Mark's treachery, Sir Dinas promised what the Queen asked, and as they devised it, so it was done. Sir Tristram was delivered out of prison, and immediately in all haste he and La Belle Iseult took ship and went by water to England.

When Sir Lancelot knew of their coming he was glad beyond measure, and he and Sir Tristram had great joy of each other. He took Sir Tristram and La Belle Iseult to Joyous Gard, his own castle, which he had won with his own hands, and there he put them in to possess it for their own. That castle was garnished and furnished so that a royal King and Queen might have sojourned there. And Sir Lancelot charged all his people to honor them and love them, as he did himself.

And there safe from the treacherous wiles of "King Fox," after all their trials and dangers, Sir Tristram and La Belle Iseult dwelt for many days in happiness and peace.

THE QUEST OF THE HOLY GRAIL

THE SIEGE PERILOUS

Now we will leave Sir Tristram of Lyonesse, and speak of Sir Lancelot of the Lake, and Sir Galahad, Sir Lancelot's son.

Before the time when Galahad was born there came a hermit to King Arthur, on Whitsunday, as the knights sat at the Round Table. Now there was one seat at the Round Table which always stood empty, and it was called "the Siege (or seat) Perilous." When the hermit saw this seat he asked the King and all the knights why it was empty.

"There is never anyone who shall sit in that seat without being destroyed, except one person," was the answer.

"Do you know who that is?" asked the hermit.

"Nay," said Arthur, and all the knights, "we know not who he is that shall sit therein."

"Then I know," said the hermit. "He that shall sit there is not yet born; and this year, he that is to sit there, in the Siege Perilous, shall be born. And he shall win the Holy Grail."

When the hermit said this he departed from the Court of King Arthur.

After this feast Sir Lancelot rode on his adventures, till one day by chance he passed over the bridge of Corbin, and there he saw the fairest tower he had ever seen, and under it was a beautiful town full of people; and all the people, men and women, cried at once:

246

"Welcome, Sir Lancelot of the Lake, flower of all knighthood, for by thee we shall be helped out of danger."

Sir Lancelot asked why they thus called upon him, whereupon the people replied that a fair lady was cruelly shut up in a hot room in the tower, and no one but himself could deliver her. Sir Lancelot, therefore, went to the tower, and when he came to the chamber where the lady was, the iron doors unlocked and unbolted themselves. He went into the room, which was as hot as any furnace, and there he found a beautiful lady, and he took her by the hand. By enchantment Queen Morgan le Fay and the Queen of North Wales had put her into this hot room, because she was called the fairest lady of that country. There she had been five years, and never might be delivered out of her pain until the time when the best knight of the world had taken her by the hand.

When she found herself rescued from the wicked spell, the lady asked Sir Lancelot to go with her into a church, to give God thanks for her deliverance. This having been done, and all the people, learned and unlearned, having given thanks, they said to Lancelot, "Sir Knight, since ye have delivered this lady, ye shall deliver us from a serpent that is here in a tomb."

Sir Lancelot took his shield, and said, "Bring me thither, and what I can do to please God and yourselves, that will I do."

The people led him to the place, and there he saw written on the tomb letters of gold, which said thus:

"Here shall come a leopard of King's blood, and he shall slay this serpent, and this leopard shall have a son, a lion, in this foreign country, the which lion shall pass all other knights."

Sir Lancelot lifted up the tomb, and out sprang a horrible and fiendish dragon, spitting fire from his mouth. The dragon flew at Sir Lancelot, but the knight fell upon him with his sword, and at last, after a long fight, with great pain he slew him.

Therewith came King Pelles, the good and noble knight, and saluted Sir Lancelot, and he him again.

"Fair knight," said the King, "what is your name?"

"Sir, wit you well, my name is Lancelot of the Lake."

"And my name," said the King, "is Pelles, King of this country; and I am of the family of Joseph of Arimathea."

Then each made much of the other, and so they went into the Castle to take their repast. And straightway here came in a dove at a window, and in her mouth there seemed a little censer of gold; immediately there was such a savor as if all the spicery of the world had been there, and forthwith on the table were all manner of meats and drinks that they could think of.

Then in came a damsel, passing young and fair, and she bore a vessel of gold betwixt her hands. The King knelt down devoutly and said his prayers, and so did all who were there.

"What may this mean?" said Sir Lancelot.

"That is the most precious thing that ever living man hath," said King Pelles. "And when the fame of this thing goeth about, the Round Table shall be broken. Wit thou well, this is the Holy Grail that ye have seen."

Now King Pelles had a daughter, as fair a lady, and young, and as wise as any at that time living; her name was Elaine. When Sir Lancelot slew the dragon, King Pelles knew that the words written in letters of gold on the tomb would come true. For "the leopard of King's blood" who came into the foreign country meant Sir Lancelot himself; and "the lion" who was to surpass all other knights was Sir Galahad, who was no other than the son of Sir Lancelot of the Lake and the Lady Elaine, daughter of King Pelles.

HOW GALAHAD WAS MADE KNIGHT

Fifteen years had gone by since that Whitsunday when King Arthur and his knights held festival at Camelot, and the hermit had foretold who it was that was to sit in the Siege Perilous. And for all those years the Siege Perilous had still stood empty.

Once again it was the vigil of Pentecost, when all the fellowship of the Round Table had come to Camelot to renew their vows and take part in the holy service. The tables were set ready for the feast when right into the hall entered a fair gentlewoman, who had ridden full fast, for her horse was covered with sweat.

She alighted, and came before King Arthur, and saluted him; and he said, "Damsel, God bless thee!"

"Sir," she said, "I pray you tell me where Sir Lancelot is."

"Yonder you may see him," said the King.

Then she went to Lancelot, and said, "Sir Lancelot, I salute you on King Pelles' behalf, and I require you to come with me to a forest hereby."

Sir Lancelot asked her with whom she dwelt.

"I dwell with King Pelles," she answered.

"What will you with me?" asked Sir Lancelot.

"You shall know when you come thither."

"Well," said he, "I will gladly go with you."

So Sir Lancelot bade his squire saddle his horse, and bring his arms, and in all haste the man did his command.

Then came Queen Guinevere to Lancelot, and said, "Will you leave us at this high feast?"

"Madam," said the gentlewoman, "wit you well, he shall be with you again tomorrow by dinnertime."

"If I knew he would not be with us here tomorrow," said the Queen, "he should not go with you by my good will."

Right so departed Sir Lancelot with the gentlewoman. They rode until they came to a forest, and into a great valley, where they saw an abbey of nuns. A squire was ready who opened the gates, so they entered and descended off their horses, and a fair company came about Sir Lancelot, and welcomed him, and were passing glad of his coming.

They led him into the abbess's chamber, and unarmed him, and there he found two of his cousins, Sir Bors and Sir Lionel, who were greatly rejoiced and astonished to see him.

"Sir," said Sir Bors, "what adventure hath brought thee hither, for we thought tomorrow to have found thee at Camelot?"

"Truly," said Sir Lancelot, "a gentlewoman brought me hither, but I know not the cause."

In the meanwhile, as they thus stood talking together, there came twelve nuns, who brought with them a boy of about fifteen years old, so beautiful and well made, that scarcely in the world could man find his match. And all those ladies were weeping.

"Sir," they said, "we bring you here this child, Galahad, whom we have nourished, and we pray you to make him a knight; for of no worthier man's hand could he receive the order of knighthood."

Sir Lancelot beheld that young squire, and saw him

seemly and demure as a dove, with all manner of good features, so that he thought he had never seen a man of his age so fair of face and form.

Then said Sir Lancelot, "Cometh this desire of himself?" And the boy and all the nuns said "Yea!"

"Then shall he receive the high order of knighthood tomorrow at the reverence of the high feast," said Lancelot.

That night Sir Lancelot had passing good cheer, and on the morrow, at the hour of dawn, at Galahad's desire, he made him knight.

"God made you a good man," said Sir Lancelot, "for beauty failest you not, as any that liveth. Now, fair sir, will you come with me to the Court of King Arthur?"

"Nay," said the boy, "I will not go with you at this time."

So Sir Lancelot departed from the Abbey, and took his two cousins with him, and they came to Camelot by nine o'clock in the morning on Whitsunday. By that time the King and the Queen had gone to the minster to hear the service. When the King and all the knights came back, the Barons saw that the seats of the Round Table were all written about with gold letters—here one ought to sit, and here ought another to sit.

Thus they went along until they came to the Siege Perilous, where they found letters of gold, newly written, which said:

"Four hundred winters and fifty-four after the passion of our Lord Jesus Christ, ought this Siege to be filled."

Then they all said, "This is a marvellous thing, and an adventurous."

"By heaven it is," said Sir Lancelot; and then he counted the period of the writing from the time of our Lord to that day. "It seems to me," he said, "this siege ought to be filled this same day, for this is the Feast of Pentecost after the four hundredth and fifty-fourth year. And if it would please all parties, I counsel that none of these letters be seen this day, until he cometh who ought to achieve this adventure."

Then they ordered a cloth of silk to be brought to cover these letters in the Siege Perilous, after which King Arthur made them haste to dinner.

"Sir," said Sir Kay, the steward, "if you go now to your meat, you will break the old custom of your Court. For you are not used on this day to sit down to table before you have seen some adventure."

"You speak truth," said the King, "but I had so great joy of Sir Lancelot, and of his cousins, who are come to the Court whole and sound, that I bethought me not of my old custom."

As they stood speaking, in came a squire.

"Sir," said he to the King, "I bring to you marvellous tidings."

"What are they?" said the King.

"Sir, there is here beneath, at the river, a great stone, which I saw float above the water, and therein I saw sticking a sword."

"I will see that marvel," said the King.

So all the knights went with him, and when they came to the river, they found there a stone floating, as it were of red marble, and therein stuck a fair and rich sword, in the pommel of which were precious stones, wrought with subtle letters of gold.

Then the Barons read the letters, which said in this wise:

"Never shall man take me hence but he by whose side I ought to hang, and he shall be the best knight of the world."

When King Arthur saw these letters he said to Sir Lancelot:

"Fair sir, this sword ought to be yours, for I am sure you are the best knight in the world."

But Sir Lancelot answered full soberly:

"Certes, sir, it is not my sword; also, wit you well, I have no hardihood to set my hand to it, for it belongeth not to hang by my side. Also, whoever assayeth to take that sword, and faileth of it, he shall receive from it a wound, of which long afterwards he shall not be whole. And I will that ye take note that this same day the adventure of the Holy Grail will begin."

MARVELS, AND GREATER MARVELS

THEN King Arthur asked his nephew Sir Gawaine to try to draw the sword from the stone in the river. But Sir Gawaine said he could not do it. Then the King commanded him to make the attempt.

"Sir," said Gawaine, "since you command me I will obey." Therewith he took the sword by the handle, but he could not stir it.

"I thank you," said the King.

"My lord Sir Gawaine," said Sir Lancelot, "now wit you well, this sword shall touch you so sore that you shall wish you had never set your hand to it, for the best castle of this realm."

"I could not withstay my uncle's will and command," said Gawaine.

King Arthur hearing this, repented greatly what he had done, nevertheless he asked Sir Percival to assay it, for his love.

"Gladly, to bear Sir Gawaine fellowship," replied Sir Percival, and therewith he set his hand on the sword, and drew it strongly, but he could not move it. Then there were others who dared to be so bold as to set their hands to it.

"Now you may go to your dinner," said Sir Kay to the King, "for a marvellous adventure have you seen."

So the King and all went back to the Palace, and every knight knew his own place, and sat therein, and young men who were knights served them.

When they were served, and the seats filled, save only the Siege Perilous, there suddenly befell a marvellous adventure —all the doors and windows shut of themselves. Yet the hall was not greatly darkened because of this, and they were one and all amazed.

King Arthur was the first to speak.

"Fair fellows and lords," he said, "we have seen this day marvels, but before night I expect we shall see greater marvels."

In the meanwhile came in a good old man, very ancient, clothed all in white, and no knight knew from whence he came. He brought with him a young knight, also on foot, in red armor, without sword or shield, but with only a scabbard hanging by his side.

"Peace be with you, lords!" said the old man. Then, to Arthur, "Sir, I bring here a young knight, who is of King's lineage, and of the kindred of Joseph of Arimathea, whereby the marvels of this Court and of strange realms shall be fully accomplished."

The King was very pleased at his words, and said to the old man, "Sir, you are right welcome, and the young knight with you."

The old man made the young knight take off his armor, and under it he was clad in a coat of red silk, and the old man put on him a mantle furred with ermine. Then saying to the young knight, "Sir, follow me," he led him straight to the Siege Perilous, beside which sat Sir Lancelot. The good man lifted up the silken cloth, and underneath it he found letters which said thus:

"This is the seat of Galahad, the high prince."

"Sir, wit you well that place is yours," said the old man, and he made him sit down surely in that seat.

Then the young knight said to the old man, "Sir, you may now go your way, for you have done well what you were commanded to do. And commend me to my grandsire, King Pelles, and say to him on my behalf that I will come and see him as soon as ever I can."

So the good man departed, and there were waiting for him twenty noble squires, and they took their horses and went their way.

All the Knights of the Round Table marvelled greatly at Galahad, because he had dared to sit there in that Siege Perilous, and he was so tender of age. They knew not from whence he came, but only that God had sent him, and they said:

"This is he by whom the Holy Grail shall be achieved, for never anyone but he sat in that place without mischief befalling him."

But Sir Lancelot beheld his son, and had great joy of him.

"By my life, this young knight shall come to great honor," said Sir Bors to his companions.

There was great excitement in all the Palace, so that the news came to Queen Guinevere. She marvelled what knight it could be who ventured to sit in the Siege Perilous. Then many told her that he much resembled Sir Lancelot.

"I can well imagine," said the Queen, "that he is son of Sir Lancelot and King Pelles' daughter, and his name is Galahad. I would fain see him, for he must needs be a noble man, for so is his father."

When the meal was over, so that King Arthur and all

were risen, the King went to the Siege Perilous, and lifted up the cloth, and found there the name of Galahad. He showed it to Sir Gawaine, saying:

"Fair nephew, now we have among us Sir Galahad, who shall bring honor to us all; and on pain of my life he shall achieve the Holy Grail, right so as Sir Lancelot hath given us to understand."

Then King Arthur went to Galahad, and said, "Sir, you are welcome, for you shall move many good knights to the Quest of the Holy Grail, and you shall achieve that which never knight could do." Then the King took him by the hand, and went down from the Palace to show Galahad the adventure of the stone in the river.

Queen Guinevere, hearing this, came after with many ladies, and showed them the stone where it moved on the water.

"Here is as great a marvel as ever I saw," said King Arthur to Galahad, "and right good knights have assayed and failed."

"Sir, that is no marvel," said Galahad, "for this adventure is not theirs, but mine, and with the certainty of this sword, I brought none with me; for here by my side hangeth the scabbard." He laid his hand on the sword, and lightly drew it out of the stone, and put it in the sheath. "Now it goeth better than it did before."

"God will send you a shield," said the King.

"Now have I that sword which was sometime that good knight's, Balin the Savage," said Galahad, "and he was a passing good man of his hands. With this sword he slew his unknown brother Balan, and that was a great pity, for he was a good knight; and each slew the other, not knowing they were brothers, because of a dolorous stroke that Balan gave my grandfather, King Pelles, which is not yet whole, nor shall be till I heal him."

At that moment the King and all espied a lady on a white palfrey, who came riding down the river towards them. She saluted the King and the Queen, and asked if Sir Lancelot were there. He answered himself, "I am here, fair lady."

Then she said, all weeping:

"How your great doing is changed since this day in the morning!"

"Damsel, why say you so?" said Lancelot.

"I say the truth," said the damsel, "for this morning you were the best knight in the world; but who should say so now would be a liar, for now there is one better than you. And this is well proved by the adventure of the sword, whereto you dared not set your hand; and hence comes the change and leaving of your name. Wherefore I bid you remember that you shall not ween from henceforth that you are the best knight of the world."

"As touching that," said Sir Lancelot, "I know well I was never the best."

"Yes," said the damsel; "that you were; and are so yet, of any sinful man of the world. And, Sir King, Nacien the hermit sendeth thee word that there shall befall thee the greatest honor that ever befell King in Britain. And I will tell you wherefore. This day the Holy Grail shall appear in thy house, and feed thee, and all thy fellowship of the Round Table."

So the damsel departed and went back the same way that she had come.

THE LAST TOURNAMENT

"Now," said King Arthur, "I am sure that all ye of the Round Table will depart on this quest of the Holy Grail, and never shall I see the whole of you again all together. Therefore will I see you all together in the meadow of Camelot, to joust and to tourney, that after your death men may speak of it, that such knights were wholly together on such a day."

To that counsel and the King's request they all agreed, and put on their armor that belonged to jousting. But the King did this with the intent of seeing Galahad proved, for the King deemed he would not lightly come to the Court again after his departing.

So they all assembled in the meadow, and the Queen was in a tower with all her ladies to behold that tournament. Then Galahad, at the King's entreaty, put on a noble cuirass, and also his helm, but shield he would take none, not for any entreaty of the King.

Sir Gawaine and the other knights prayed him to take a spear, and this he did. Then taking his place in the midst of the meadow he began to break spears marvellously, so that all men wondered at him. For he there surpassed all other knights, and in a little while had thrown down many good Knights of the Round Table. But Sir Lancelot and Sir Percival he did not overthrow.

King Arthur, at Queen Guinevere's request, made him alight and unlace his helm, so that the Queen might see his face. And when she beheld him she said, "Truly I dare well say that Sir Lancelot is his father, for never two men were more alike; therefore it is no marvel if he be of great prowess."

A lady that stood by the Queen said:

"Madam, ought he of right to be so good a knight?"

"Yes, in truth," said the Queen, "for both from his father's and his mother's side he is come of the best knights of the world, and of the highest lineage. I dare affirm that Sir Lancelot and Sir Galahad are the greatest gentlemen of the world."

Then the King and all the nobles went home to Camelot, and after they had been to evensong in the great minster, they went to supper; and every knight sat in his own place as they had done before.

Suddenly they heard crackling and rolling of thunder, as if the place would have been riven. In the midst of this blast entered a sunbeam, clearer by seven times than ever they saw by day, and all their faces shone with a divine light. Then began every knight to look at each other, and each seemed fairer than any one had seemed before. Not a knight could speak a single word for a great while, so they looked every man at each other, as if they had been dumb.

Then there entered into the hall the Holy Grail, covered with white samite, but none could see it, nor who bore it. And all the hall was filled with good odors, and every knight had such meats and drinks as he liked best; and when the Holy Grail had been borne through the hall, then the holy vessel departed suddenly, so that they knew not what became of it.

After it had gone they all had breath to speak, and King Arthur gave thanks to God for the great favor He had sent them.

"Now," said Sir Gawaine, "we have been served this day with what meats and drinks we thought of, but one thing hath failed us,—we could not see the Holy Grail, it was covered with such care. Therefore I will here make a vow, that tomorrow without longer abiding I shall undertake the Quest of the Holy Grail. I shall hold out a twelvemonth and a day, or more, if need be, and never shall I return again to the Court till I have seen it more openly than it hath been seen here. And if I do not succeed, I shall return again as one that cannot act against the will of heaven."

When the Knights of the Round Table heard what Sir Gawaine said, most of them rose up, and made the same sort of vow as Sir Gawaine had made.

King Arthur was greatly displeased at this, for he knew well they might not gainsay their vows.

"Alas," he said to Sir Gawaine, "you have almost slain me with the vow and promise you have made. For through you, ye have reft me of the fairest fellowship, and the truest of knighthood that ever were seen together in any realm of the world. For when my knights depart hence I am sure that never more will they all meet together in this world, for many of them shall die in the Quest. And so I repent it, for I have loved them as well as my life, wherefore it shall grieve me right sore, the breaking up of this fellowship. For this is an old custom that I have had kept."

And therewith his eyes filled with tears.

"Oh, Gawaine, Gawaine," he said, "you have set me in great sorrow. For I doubt much that my true fellowship shall ever more meet here again."

"Comfort yourself," said Lancelot, "for if we die in the Quest it shall be to us as a great honor, and much more than if we had died in any other place; for early or late, of death we are sure."

"Ah, Lancelot," said the King, "the great love I have had for you all the days of my life maketh me to say such doleful words. For never Christian King had so many worthy men at his table, as I have had this day at the Round Table, and that is my great sorrow."

When the Queen, ladies, and gentlewomen knew these tidings they had such sorrow and heaviness that no tongue could tell it, for those knights had holden them in honor and love. But among all the others Queen Guinevere made most sorrow.

"I marvel," said she, "that my lord, the King, would suffer them to depart from him."

Thus all the Court were troubled, because of the departing of those knights. Some of the ladies who loved knights, wanted to go with their husbands and lovers, and would have done so, had not an aged knight in religious clothing come among them.

"Fair lords, who have sworn to the Quest of the Holy Grail," he said, "Nacien the hermit thus sendeth you word, that none in this Quest lead lady or gentlewoman, for it is a hard and high service. Moreover, I warn you that he who is not clean of his sins shall not see these mysteries."

After this, the Queen came to Galahad, and asked him whence he was, and of what country. He told her.

"And son unto Lancelot?" she asked; but to this he said neither yea nor nay.

"Truly," said the Queen, "of your father you need not be ashamed, for he is the goodliest knight, and come of the best men of the world, on both sides of a race of Kings. Wherefore you ought of right to be of your deeds a passing good man,—and certainly you resemble him much."

Galahad was a little abashed at this, and said:

"Madam, since you know it for certain, why did you ask me? For he that is my father shall be known openly, and in good time."

Then they all went to rest. And in honor of Galahad's greatness and high race he was led into King Arthur's chamber, and rested on the King's own bed.

As soon as it was day the King arose, for he had no rest all that night for sorrow. Then he went to Gawaine and Sir Lancelot, who had arisen to go to church.

"Ah, Gawaine, Gawaine," said the King, "you have betrayed me. For never shall my Court be amended by you; but you will never be as sorry for me as I am for you." And therewith the tears began to run down his face. "Ah, knight, Sir Lancelot," he said, "I pray thee counsel me, for I would this Quest were undone, if it could be."

"Sir," said Lancelot, "ye saw yesterday so many worthy knights who were then sworn so that they cannot leave it in any sort of way."

"That I know well," said the King. "But I grieve so at their departing that I know well no manner of joy shall ever cure me."

Then the King and the Queen went to the minster.

Lancelot and Gawaine commanded their men to bring their arms, and when they were all armed save their shields and their helms they were ready in the same wise to go to the minster to hear the service.

After the service the King wished to know how many had undertaken the Quest of the Holy Grail; and they found by counting, it was a hundred and fifty, and all were Knights of the Round Table.

Then they put on their helms ready to depart, and commended them all wholly to the Queen, and there was weeping and great sorrow. And Queen Guinevere went into her chamber, so that no one should see her great grief.

Sir Lancelot missing the Queen, went to look for her, and when she saw him, she cried aloud:

"O, Sir Lancelot, you have forsaken us! You put me to death thus to leave my lord!"

"Ah, madam," said Sir Lancelot, "I pray you be not displeased, for I shall come again as soon as I can in accordance with my honor."

"Alas," said she, "that ever I saw you! But He that suffered death upon the Cross for all mankind be your good conduct and safety, and that of all the whole fellowship!"

Right so departed Sir Lancelot, and found his companions who awaited his coming. They mounted their horses, and rode through the streets of Camelot, and there was weeping of the rich and poor, and the King turned away, and could not speak for weeping.

So the Knights of the Round Table rode forth on the Quest of the Holy Grail.

That night they rested in a Castle called Vagon, where the lord was a good old man, and made them the best cheer he could. On the morrow they all agreed they should each separate from the other. So the next day, with weeping and mourning, they departed, and every knight took the way that seemed to him best.

SIR GALAHAD'S WHITE SHIELD

Now Galahad was yet without a shield, and he rode four days without adventure.

On the fourth day after evensong he came to an abbey of white friars, and there he was received with great reverence, and led to a chamber, and unarmed. Then he was aware of two Knights of the Round Table, one was Sir Bagdemagus, the other was Sir Uwaine; and they were very pleased to see him.

"Sirs," said Galahad, "what adventures brought you hither?"

"It is told us," they replied, "that in this place is a shield that no man may bear about his neck, without being hurt or dead within three days, or else maimed forever."

"I shall bear it tomorrow to assay this strange adventure," added King Bagdemagus to Galahad, "and if I cannot achieve this advenutre of the shield, ye shall take it upon you, for I am sure you shall not fail."

"I agree right well to that," said Galahad, "for I have no shield."

On the morrow they arose, and after hearing service, King Bagdemagus asked where the adventurous shield was. A monk at once led him behind an altar, where the shield hung. It was white as any snow, but in the midst was a red cross.

"Sir," said the monk, "this shield ought not to hang round the neck of any knight, unless he be the worthiest knight of the world, therefore I counsel you knights to be well advised."

"Well," said King Bagdemagus, "I know well I am not the best knight of the world, but yet I shall assay to bear it."

So he bore it out of the monastery, saying to Galahad, "If it please you, I pray you abide here still, till you know how I shall speed."

"I will await you here," said Galahad.

King Bagdemagus took with him a squire to carry back tidings to Galahad how he sped. When they had ridden about two miles they came to a fair valley before a hermitage, and there they saw coming from that direction a goodly knight, in white armor, horse, and all. He came as fast as his horse could run, with his spear in the rest, and King Bagdemagus dressed his spear against him, and broke it upon the white knight. But the other struck him so hard that he shattered the mail, and thrust him through the right shoulder, for just there the shield did not cover him, and so he bore him from his horse.

Then the knight alighted, and took the white shield from Bagdemagus, saying:

"Knight, thou hast done thyself great folly, for this shield ought not to be borne but my him that shall have no peer that liveth."

Then he came to King Bagdemagus' squire and said, "Bear this shield to the good knight Sir Galahad, whom thou left in the abbey, and greet him well from me."

"Sir," said the squire, "what is your name?"

"Take thou no heed of my name," said the knight, "for it is not for thee to know, nor any earthly man."

"Now, fair sir," said the squire, "for the love of heaven, tell me for what cause this shield may not be borne, without the bearer thereof coming to mischief."

"Since thou hast conjured me so," said the knight, "this

shield belongeth to no man but Galahad."

The squire went to King Bagdemagus and asked if he were sore wounded or not.

"Yea, forsooth," he said, "I shall hardly escape death."

The squire fetched his horse, and took him with great pain to an abbey. There he was gently unarmed, and laid in a bed, and his wounds were looked to. And there he lay a long while, and hardly escaped with life.

The squire carried the shield to Galahad, with the knight's message.

"Now blessed be God and fortune," said Galahad. Then he asked for his armor, and mounted his horse, and hung the white shield about his neck, and bade them good-bye. Sir Uwaine said he would bear him fellowship if it pleased him, but Galahad replied that he could not do so, for he must go alone except for the squire that went with him.

Within a little while Sir Galahad came near the hermitage, and there was the white knight awaiting him. Each saluted the other courteously, and then the strange knight told him the legend of the white shield.

It had been made over four hundred years ago by Joseph of Arimathea for a King called Evelake, who was at war with the Saracens. On the eve of a great battle Joseph of Arimathea went to King Evelake, and showed him the right belief of the Christian faith, to which he agreed with all his heart. Then this shield was made for King Evelake, and through it he got the better of his enemies. For when he went into battle there was a cloth placed over the shield, and when he found himself in the greatest peril, he drew aside the cloth, and then his enemies saw the cross, and were all discomfited.

Afterwards befell a strange marvel, for the cross on the

shield vanished away, so that no man knew what became of it.

At the end of the war King Evelake was baptized, and so were most of the people in his city. And when Joseph of Arimathea departed, King Evelake insisted on going with him, whether he would or not. So it chanced they came to this land, which at that time was called Great Britain.

Not long after Joseph of Arimathea fell ill, and was like to die. King Evelake was deeply grieved, and prayed him to leave some token of remembrance. "That will I do full gladly," said the holy man, and he bade him bring the shield, which was now quite white. Then with his own blood Joseph of Arimathea traced on it a red cross.

"Now you may see a remembrance that I love you," he said, "for you shall never see this shield but you shall think of me. And it shall be always as fresh as it is now. And never shall any man bear this shield round his neck but he shall repent it, until the time that Galahad the good knight bear it, and the last of my lineage shall have it about his neck, and shall do many marvellous deeds."

"Now," said King Evelake, "where shall I put this shield, that this worthy knight may have it?"

"You shall leave it there where Nacien the hermit shall be put after his death. For thither shall that good knight come the fifth day after he receives the order of knighthood."

"So that day which they appointed is this time that you have received the shield," said the knight to Galahad. "And in the same abbey lieth Nacien the hermit. And you are a grandson of King Pelles, who is of the race of Joseph of Arimathea."

And with that the White Knight vanished away.

THE ADVENTURE OF THE CROWN OF GOLD

As soon as the squire heard what the White Knight said to Sir Galahad he alighted off his hackney, and kneeling down at Galahad's feet, prayed that he might go with him till he had made him knight. "And that order, by the grace of God, shall be well held by me," he added. So Sir Galahad granted his petition. Then they returned to the abbey where they had come from, and great joy was made of Sir Galahad, and there he rested that night.

On the morrow he knighted the squire, and asked him his name, and of what kindred he was come.

"Sir," said he, "men call me Melias of the Isle, and I am a son of the King of Denmark."

"Now, fair sir," said Galahad, "since ye be come of Kings and Queens, look you that knighthood be well set in you, for you ought to be a mirror to all chivalry."

"Sir, you say truth," said Melias. "But since you have made me a knight you must by right grant me my first desire, if it is reasonable."

"That is true," said Galahad.

"Then will you suffer me to ride with you in this Quest of the Holy Grail?" asked Melias.

And Galahad granted it.

His armor, his spear, and his horse were then brought to Sir Melias, but Sir Galahad and he rode forth all that week before they found any adventure.

On a Monday, in the morning, after leaving an abbey, they came to a cross which parted two ways, and on that cross were letters written, which said thus:

"Now ye knights-errant, who go to seek knights adventurous, see here two ways: one way it is forbidden thee to go, for none shall come out of that way again, unless he be a good man and a worthy knight; if thou go this way on the left hand, thou shalt not there lightly win prowess, for thou shalt in this way be soon assayed."

"Sir," said Melias to Galahad, "if it please you to suffer me to take this way on the left hand, tell me, for there I shall well test my strength."

"It were better ye rode not that way," said Galahad, "for I deem I should escape better in that way than you."

"Nay, my lord, I pray you let me have that adventure."

"Take it, in heaven's name," said Galahad.

Then Melias rode into an old forest, through which he travelled two days and more, till he came to a green meadow, where there was a fair lodge of boughs. And he espied in the lodge a chair, wherein was a crown of gold, subtly wrought. Also, there were cloths spread upon the ground, on which were set many delicious meats.

Sir Melias beheld this adventure, and thought it marvellous. He had no hunger, but he had great desire of the crown of gold, so he stooped down, took it up, and rode his way with it. Soon he saw a knight come riding after him, who said:

"Knight, set down that crown of gold, which is not yours, and therefore defend yourself!"

"Fair Lord of Heaven, help and save Thy new-made knight!" prayed Sir Melias.

Then they urged on their horses as fast as they could, and the other knight smote Sir Melias through hauberk, and through the left side, so that he fell to the earth nearly dead. The knight took the crown of gold and went his way, and Sir Melias lay still and had no power to stir.

In the meanwhile, by good fortune, came Sir Galahad, and found him there in peril of death.

"Ah, Melias, who hath wounded you?" he said. "It would have been better to have ridden the other way."

"Sir, for God's love let me not die in this forest," said Melias, "but bear me to the abbey here beside, that I may be confessed and have heavenly comfort."

"It shall be done," said Galahad; "but where is he that hath wounded you?"

At that moment Sir Galahad heard through the trees a loud cry—"Knight, keep thee from me!"

"Ah, sir, beware!" said Melias, "for that is he who hath slain me."

"Sir Knight, come at your peril!" answered Sir Galahad.

Then each turned towards the other, and they came together as fast as their horses could run, and Galahad smote the stranger so that his spear went through his shoulder, and bore him down off his horse, and in the falling Galahad's spear broke. With that, out came another knight from among the trees, and broke a spear upon Galahad, before ever he could turn. Then Galahad drew out his sword, and smote off his left arm, whereupon the knight fled.

After chasing him for some distance Sir Galahad returned to Melias, and placing him gently on his horse, sprang up behind, and held him in his arms, and so brought him to the abbey. There his wound was carefully tended, and an old monk, who had once been a knight, told Sir Galahad he hoped it would be healed within about seven weeks. Sir Galahad was glad to hear this, and said he would stay at the abbey for three days.

At the end of that time he said, "Now I will depart, for I have much on hand; many good knights are full busy about it, and this knight and I were in the same Quest of the Holy Grail."

"For his sin was he thus wounded," said a good man. "And I marvel," he added to Melias, "how you dare take upon you so rich a thing as the high order of knighthood without clean confession, and that was the cause you were bitterly wounded. For the road on the right hand betokeneth the highway of our Lord Jesus Christ, and the way of a true, good liver. And the other road betokeneth the way of sinners and misbelievers. And when the devil saw your pride and presumption tempt you into the Quest of the Holy Grail, that made you to be overthrown, for it may not be achieved but by a virtuous living."

"Also, the writing on the cross was a signification of heavenly deeds, and of knightly deeds in God's works, and no knightly deeds in worldly works; and pride is head of all deadly sins, which caused thee, Melias, to depart from Sir Galahad. And when thou tookest the crown of gold, thou sinnedst in covetousness and theft. All these were no knightly deeds, and this Galahad, the holy knight, who fought with the two knights,—the two knights signify the two deadly sins pride and covetousness, which were wholly in Sir Melias, and they could not stand against Sir Galahad, for he is without deadly sin."

Now departed Galahad from them, and bade them all good-bye.

"My lord Galahad," said Melias, "as soon as I can ride, I shall seek you."

"God send you health," said Galahad, and so took his horse and departed.

THE CASTLE OF MAIDENS

Sir Galahad rode many journeys, backward and forward, as adventure led him, and at last one day he came to a mountain, where he found an old chapel, and nobody there, for all was desolate. Then he knelt before the altar, and prayed for good counsel, and as he prayed he heard a voice that said, "Go thou now, thou adventurous knight, to the Castle of Maidens, and there do away with the wicked customs."

When Sir Galahad heard this, he thanked God and took his horse. He had ridden only half-a-mile when he saw in a valley before him a strong Castle, with deep ditches; beside it ran a fair river, called the Severn, and there he met with a very old man. Each saluted the other, and Galahad asked him the Castle's name.

"Fair sir," he said, "it is the Castle of Maidens."

"That is a cursed Castle," said Galahad, "and all they who are connected with it, for all pity is outside it, and all boldness and mischief are within."

"For that reason I counsel you, sir knight, to turn again."

"Sir, wit you well I shall not turn again," said Sir Galahad. Then he looked to his arms that nothing failed him, and put his shield before him, and at that moment there met him seven fair maidens.

"Sir Knight," they said, "you ride here in great folly, for you have the river to pass over."

"Why should I not pass the river?" said Galahad. So he rode away from them.

Next there met him a squire, who said:

"Knight, those knights in the Castle defy you, and forbid you to go further till they know what you want."

"Fair sir, I come to destroy the wicked custom of this Castle."

"Sir, if you keep to that, you will have enough to do."

"Go you now," said Galahad, "and hasten my needs."

Then the squire entered into the Castle. And immediately after, there came out of the Castle seven knights, who were all brethren. When they saw Galahad, they cried, "Knight, keep thee, for we assure thee nothing but death!"

"Why, will you all fight with me at once?" said Galahad.

"Yea," said they, "you may trust to that."

Galahad thrust forth his spear, and struck the foremost to the earth, so that he nearly broke his neck, whereupon all the other brothers smote him on his shield great strokes, so that their spears broke. Then Galahad drew out his sword and set upon them so hard that it was a marvel to see, and thus through great might he made them forsake the field. As they fled, he chased them till they entered into the Castle, and passing right through the Castle, escaped out of another gate.

Now there met Sir Galahad an old man, clad in religious clothing, who said, "Sir, have here the keys of the Castle." Then Galahad opened the gates, and so many people came thronging round him that he could not number them.

"Sir," they all said, "you are welcome, for long have we waited here our deliverance."

Then came to him a gentlewoman. "These knights are fled," said she, "but they will come again this night, and begin again their evil customs."

"What will you that I shall do?" asked Galahad.

"That you send after all the knights to come hither who hold their lands of this Castle, and make them swear to use the customs that were formerly used here in the old times."

"I will gladly," said Galahad.

She brought him a horn of ivory, richly bound with gold, and said, "Sir, blow this horn; it will be heard two miles round the Castle."

When Galahad had blown the horn he went to rest, and presently there came a priest, who told him the story of the Castle.

"It is just seven years ago," he said, "that these seven brethren came to this Castle, and lodged with the lord of it, who was called the Duke Lianor, and who was lord of all this country. When they espied the duke's daughter, who was a very beautiful woman, they began to weave false plots as to which should marry her, till they took to quarrelling among themselves. The duke in his goodness would have parted them, but in their anger they slew him and his eldest son. Then they seized the maiden, and the treasure of the Castle. Afterwards, by great strength they held all the knights of this Castle in great bondage and extortion, besides robbing and plundering the poor country people of all that they had. So it happened on a day the duke's daughter said, 'You have done me great wrong, to slay my own father and my brother, and thus to hold our lands. But you shall not hold this Castle for many years, for by one knight you shall be overcome.' Thus she prophesied seven years ago. 'Well,' said the seven knights, 'since you say so, never lady nor knight shall pass this Castle, but they shall abide here, in spite of their will, or die for it, until that knight come by whom we shall lose this Castle.' Thereupon it is called the Castle of Maidens, for many fair ladies have here been destroyed."

"Now," said Galahad, "is she here for whom this Castle was lost?"

"Nay," said the priest, "she was dead within three nights after speaking the prophecy. And since then they have kept prisoner her younger sister, who with many other ladies endureth great pain and hardship."

By this time the knights of the country were come. Then Galahad made them do homage and fealty to the duke's younger daughter, who was still alive, and set them in great ease of heart. And the next morning a man brought tidings that Gawaine, Gareth, and Uwaine had slain the seven brethren.

"Well done!" said Galahad, and took his armor and his horse, and bade good-bye to the Castle of Maidens.

THE VISION AT THE CHAPEL
IN THE FOREST

AFTER leaving the Castle of Maidens, Sir Galahad rode till
he came to a waste forest, and there he met with Sir Lancelot and Sir Percival, but they did not know him, for he was
newly disguised. Sir Lancelot rode straight at him, and
broke his spear on him, and Sir Galahad smote him so
again that he bore down horse and man. Then he drew
his sword, and turned to Sir Percival, and smote him on the
helm so that it rove to the coif of steel; if the sword had not
swerved, Sir Percival would have been slain; with the
stroke he fell out of the saddle.

This joust took place before a hermitage where dwelt a
recluse, who was really aunt to Sir Percival, although he did
not know it at that moment. When she saw Sir Galahad she
said, "God be with thee, best knight of the world! Ah,
certes," she said quite loud, so that Lancelot and Percival
could hear it, "if yonder two knights had known thee as
well as I do, they would not have encountered with thee."

Galahad, hearing her say this, was sorely afraid of being
known, and therefore rode swiftly away. Then both knights
perceived he was Galahad, and up they got on their horses,
and rode fast after him, but he was soon out of sight. So
they returned with heavy cheer.

"Let us ask some tidings of yonder recluse," said Percival.

"Do so, if you please," said Lancelot, but when Percival
went to the hermitage he rode on alone. This way and that
he rode across a wild forest, and held no path except as

adventure led him. At last he came to a strong cross, which pointed two ways in waste land; by the cross was a stone that was of marble, but it was so dark that Sir Lancelot could not tell what it was.

Sir Lancelot looked about him, and near at hand he saw an old chapel, where he expected to find people. He tied his horse to a tree, and taking off his shield, hung it upon a tree. Then he went to the chapel door, but found it waste and broken. And looking within, he saw a fair altar, full richly arrayed with cloth of clean silk, where stood a shining candlestick, which bore six great candles, and the candlestick was of silver.

When Sir Lancelot saw this light he desired greatly to enter into the chapel, but could find no place where he could enter, which greatly grieved and perplexed him. He returned to his horse and took off the saddle and bridle, and let him pasture; and unlacing his helm, and ungirdling his sword, he laid himself down to sleep on his shield before the marble cross.

So he fell asleep, and half waking and half sleeping, he saw a vision.

He saw come past him two palfreys all beautiful and white, which bore a litter, and in the litter lay a sick knight. When they were near the cross the litter stood still, and Sir Lancelot heard the knight say:

"Oh, sweet Lord, when shall this sorrow leave me? And when shall the holy vessel come by, through which I shall be blessed? For I have endured thus long through little trespass."

Thus for some time lamented the knight, and Sir Lancelot heard him.

Then Sir Lancelot saw the candlestick with the six tapers

come before the marble cross, and he saw nobody that brought it. Also there came a table of silver, and the sacred vessel of the Holy Grail, which Sir Lancelot had seen formerly in King Pelles' house.

Therewith the sick knight sat up, and held up both his hands, and prayed to God, and kneeling down, he kissed the holy vessel, and immediately he was whole.

"Lord God, I thank thee, for I am healed of this sickness," he said.

So when the Holy Grail had been there a long time, it went into the chapel, with the candlestick and the lights, so that Lancelot did not know what became of it. For he was overmastered by a feeling of his own sinfulness, and had no power to rise to follow the holy vessel.

Then the sick knight rose, and kissed the cross, and the squire at once brought him his armor, and asked his lord how he did.

"Truly, I thank God, right well," he answered, "through the holy vessel I am healed. But I greatly marvel at this sleeping knight, who had no power to awake when this holy vessel was brought hither."

"I dare right well say," said the squire, "that he dwelleth in some deadly sin, whereof he has never repented."

"By my faith," said the knight, "whatsoever he be, he is unhappy, for, as I deem, he is of the fellowship of the Round Table, which has entered into the Quest of the Holy Grail."

"Sir," said the squire, "here have I brought you all your arms, save your helm and your sword, and therefore, by my advice ye may now take this knight's helm and his sword."

So the knight did this; and when he was fully armed he took also Sir Lancelot's horse, for it was better than his own. And so he and his attendants departed from the cross.

THE REPENTANCE OF SIR LANCELOT

STRAIGHTWAY Sir Lancelot awoke, and sat up, and bethought him what he had seen there, and whether it were a dream or not. Right so he heard a voice that said:

"Sir Lancelot, more hard than is the stone, and more bitter than is the wood, and more naked and bare than is the leaf of the fig-tree! Therefore go thou hence, and withdraw thee from this holy place."

When Sir Lancelot heard this, he was passing heavy, and knew not what to do; so he rose, sore weeping, and cursed the time that he was born, because he thought he would never more have honor. For those words went to his heart till he knew why he was called so.

He went to fetch his helm, his sword, and his horse, but found they had all been taken away. Then he called himself a wretch, and most unhappy of all knights. "My sin and my wickedness have brought me to great dishonor," he said. "For when I sought worldly adventures for worldly desires, I ever achieved them, and had the better in every place, and never was I discomforted in any quarrel, were it right or wrong. And now I take upon me the adventures of holy things, but I see and understand that my old sin hindereth me, and shameth me, so that I had no power to stir nor speak when the holy vessel appeared before me."

Thus he sorrowed till it was day, and he heard the little birds sing; then he was somewhat comforted.

But when he missed his horse and his arms Sir Lancelot knew well God was displeased with him. He departed from the cross on foot into the forest, and by dawn came to a high hill, where a hermit dwelt, whom he found just about to begin his morning devotions. Then Lancelot knelt down, and cried to the Lord for mercy for his wicked works. When their prayers were over, Lancelot called to the hermit, and begged him for charity to hear his life.

"Right willingly," said the good man. "Are you not of King Arthur's Court, and of the fellowship of the Round Table?"

"Yes, truly, and my name is Sir Lancelot of the Lake, who hath been right well spoken of, and now my good fortune is changed, for I am the most wretched man in the world."

The hermit looked at him, and marvelled why he was so abashed.

"Sir," said the hermit, "you ought to thank God more than any knight living, for He hath caused you to have more worldly worship than any knight that now liveth. Because of your presumption to take upon yourself, while you were still in deadly sin, to behold His holy chalice, that was the cause you might not see it with worldly eyes. For He will not appear where such sinners be, except it be to their great hurt and their great shame. And there is no knight living now who ought to give God such thanks as you. For He hath given you beauty, seemliness, and great strength, above all other knights, and therefore you are the more beholden unto God than any other man, to love Him and dread Him; for your strength and manhood will little avail you if God be against you."

Then Sir Lancelot wept for grief, and said: "Now I know well you speak truth to me."

"Sir," said the good man, "hide from me no old sin."

"Truly, I am full loath to reveal it," said Sir Lancelot. "For these fourteen years I have never revealed one thing, and for that I now blame my shame and misadventure."

And then he told that good man all his life, and how he loved a Queen beyond all measure, and had done so longer than he could reckon.

"And all my great deeds of arms that I have done, I did the most part for the Queen's sake, and for her sake would I do battle, were it right or wrong; and never did I battle only for God's sake, but to win worship, and to cause me to be the better beloved; and little or nought I thanked God for it." Then Sir Lancelot said, "I pray you counsel me."

"I will counsel you," said the hermit, "if you will assure me that you will never come into the presence of that Queen, if you can help it."

Then Sir Lancelot promised him faithfully he would not.

"Look that your heart and your mouth agree," said the good man, "and I will ensure you that you shall have more worship than ever you had."

"I marvel at the voice which said to me those strange words I told you of," said Lancelot.

"Have no marvel," said the good man, "for it seemeth well God loveth thee. Men can understand a stone is hard by nature, and one kind harder than another,—by which is meant *thee*, Sir Lancelot. For thou wilt not leave thy sin, for any goodness that God hath sent thee, therefore are thou harder than any stone; and thou wouldst never be made soft, neither by water nor by fire,—and that is, the Holy Spirit could not enter into thee. Now take heed; in all the world men shall not find one knight to whom our Lord hath given so much of grace as He hath given thee. For He hath given thee beauty, with seemliness; He hath given thee wit, discretion to know good from evil; He hath given thee prowess and hardihood; and hath given thee to work so greatly that thou hast had at all times the better whersoever thou camest. And now our Lord will suffer thee no longer, but that thou shalt know Him, whether thou wilt or wilt not.

"And why that voice called thee bitterer than wood;—where overmuch sin dwelleth, there can be but little sweetness, wherefore thou art likened to an old rotten tree. Now have I shown thee why thou art harder than the stone, and bitterer than wood.

"Now shall I show thee why thou are more naked and barer than the fig-tree. It befell that our Lord on Palm Sunday preached in Jerusalem, and there He found in the people all hardness, and there He found in all the town not one that would harbor Him. Then He went outside the town, and found in the midst of the way a fig-tree, which was right fair, and well-garnished with leaves, but fruit had it none. Then our Lord cursed the tree that bore no fruit,—and by the fig-tree was betokened Jerusalem, which had leaves and no fruit. So thou, Sir Lancelot, when the Holy Grail was brought before thee, He found in thee no fruit nor good thought, nor good will; but thou wert stained with sin."

"Verily," said Sir Lancelot, "all that you have said is true; and from henceforth I purpose by the grace of God never to be so wicked as I have been, but to follow knighthood, and do feats of arms."

Then the good man enjoined Sir Lancelot such penance as he could do, and to follow knighthood; and so he gave him blessing, and prayed Sir Lancelot to abide with him all that day.

"I will gladly," said Sir Lancelot, "for I have neither helm, nor horse, nor sword."

"As for that," said the good man, "I will help you before tomorrow evening with a horse, and all that belongs to you."

And so Sir Lancelot repented him greatly of all his past misdoings.

THE CHAMBER WITH THE SHUT DOOR

AMONG the Knights of the Round Table who started on the Quest of the Holy Grail, beside Sir Galahad and Sir Lancelot, the chief were these—the good Sir Percival; Sir Ector de Maris, brother of Sir Lancelot; Sir Bors de Ganis, and Sir Gawaine. Many and strange were the adventures that befell them, and marvellous were the visions they saw, but at no time did they come within sight of the Holy Grail. For except Sir Galahad and Sir Percival, no knight was accounted worthy to behold that divine vision.

But after the penitence of Sir Lancelot, and many long months of wandering, it at last happened to him nearly to achieve the great Quest. For one night being near the sea, a vision came to him in his sleep, and bade him enter into the first ship he could find. When he heard these words he started up, and saw a great clearness all round him, so he took his armor and made ready; and when he came to the shore he found a ship without sail or oar. As soon as he was within the ship he felt the greatest sweetness that ever he felt, and a joy that passed all earthly joy that he had ever known. And on this ship he stayed a month or more, sustained by the grace of heaven.

One day there came riding by a knight on horseback, who dismounted when he reached the ship. Then Sir Lancelot found it was his own son, Galahad, and no tongue can tell the joy they made of each other.

They told each other all the adventures and marvels that had befallen them both in many journeys since they departed from King Arthur's Court.

Lancelot and Galahad dwelt within that ship half a year, and served God daily and nightly with all their power. And often they arrived in islands far from folk, where nothing but wild beasts were to be found, and they achieved many strange adventures and perilous.

One day it befell that their ship arrived at the edge of a forest, and there they saw a knight armed all in white, richly horsed, and in his right hand he led a white horse. He came to the ship and saluted the two knights, and said:

"Galahad, sir, ye have been long enough with your father; come out of the ship, and start upon this horse, and go where adventure shall lead thee in the Quest of the Holy Grail."

Then Galahad went to his father, and kissed him tenderly, and said:

"Fair sweet father, I know not when I shall see you more, until I have seen the Holy Grail."

"I pray you," said Lancelot, "pray you to the high Father that He hold me in His service."

So Galahad took his horse, and there they heard a voice that said:

"Think to do well, for the one shall never again see the other till the dreadful day of doom."

"Now, son Galahad," said Lancelot, "since we shall part, and never see each other more, I pray the high Father to preserve both me and you."

"Sir," said Galahad, "no prayer prevaileth so much as yours," and therewith he rode away into the forest.

Then the wind arose, and for more than a month drove Lancelot through the sea, where he slept but little, but prayed to God that he might see some tidings of the Holy Grail.

It befell on a night, at midnight, that he arrived before a Castle, which on the back side was rich and fair. A postern opened towards the sea, and it was open without any warders, save that two lions kept the entry, and the moon shone clear.

Then Sir Lancelot heard a voice that said, "Lancelot, go out of this ship, and enter into this Castle, where thou shalt see a great part of thy desire."

So he ran and armed himself, and came to the gate, and saw the lions; and then he set hand to his sword, and drew it. But there came a dwarf suddenly, and smote him on the arm so sore that the sword fell out of his hand.

"Oh, man of evil faith and poor belief!" he heard a voice say, "wherefore dost thou trust more in thy weapons than in thy Maker? For He in whose service thou art, might more avail thee than thine armor."

Then said Lancelot, "I thank Thee, Lord Christ, for Thy great mercy, that Thou reprovest me of my misdeed. Now see I well that Thou holdest me for Thy servant."

Then he took his sword again, and put it up in his sheath, and signed his forehead with the cross, and came to the lions, and they made semblance to do him harm. Nevertheless he passed by them without hurt, and entered into the Castle to the chief fortress, where all the inmates seemed at rest. Then Lancelot, armed as he was, entered in, for he found no gate nor door but it was open. And at the last he found a chamber the door of which was shut; he set his hand to it, to open it, but he could not, although he put forth his utmost force to undo the door.

Then he listened and heard a voice which sang so sweetly that it seemed no earthly thing; and he thought the voice said, "Joy and honor be to the Father of Heaven!"

Then Lancelot knelt down before the chamber door, for he well knew that the Holy Grail was within that chamber, and he prayed to God that if ever he had done anything pleasing in His sight, that He would have pity on him, and show him something of what he sought.

With that, he saw the chamber door open, and there came out a great clearness, so that the house was as bright as if all the torches of the world had been there. Lancelot went to the door and would have entered, but immediately a voice said:

"Flee, Lancelot, and enter not, for thou oughtest not to do so; and if thou enter, thou shalt repent it."

So Lancelot withdrew himself back, right heavy.

Then he looked up into the midst of the chamber, and he saw a table of silver, and the holy vessel covered with red samite, and many angels about it, one of whom held a candle of wax burning. Before the holy vessel he saw a good man clothed as a priest, and it was as if a solemn service were being held. Three men stood near, and it seemed to Lancelot that the priest lifted up the youngest of them, as if to show him to the people. Lancelot marvelled not a little, for he thought that the priest was so burdened with the figure that he would fall to the ground. When he saw no one near would help the priest, Lancelot ran quickly to the door.

"Lord Christ," he said, "take it for no sin, though I help the good man, for he hath great need of help."

Right so he entered into the chamber, and went towards the table of silver; and when he came nigh, he felt a breath of air as if it were mixed with fire, and it smote him so sore in the face that it seemed to burn him, and therewith he fell to the earth, and had no power to rise. Then he felt about him many hands, which took him up, and bore him out of the chamber, and left him seemingly dead. And on the morrow he was found by the people of the Castle outside the chamber door.

Four and twenty days Sir Lancelot lay as if dead, but on the twenty-fifth day he opened his eyes. Then they told him that the Castle belonged to King Pelles, where long ago he had seen the vision of the Holy Grail for the first time. All the people marvelled when they found that this stranger was Lancelot, the good knight, and they sent word to King Pelles, who was right glad to hear the news, and went to see him, and made great joy of him. And there the king told Lancelot that his fair daughter Elaine, the mother of Galahad, was dead; and Lancelot was passing grieved to hear the tidings.

Four days Sir Lancelot stayed at the Castle, and then he took leave of King Pelles. He knew now that his Quest was ended, for that he would never see more of the Holy Grail than he had seen. So he said he would go back to the realm of Logris, which he had not seen for over a twelvemonth.

When he came to Camelot he found that some of the Knights of the Round Table had returned home, but that many of them—more than half—had been slain and destroyed.

King Arthur, Queen Guinevere, and all the Court, were passing glad to see Sir Lancelot again, and the King asked him many tidings of his son Galahad. Lancelot told the King all the adventures that had befallen him since he departed, and he also told him whatever he knew of the adventures of Galahad, Percival, and Bors.

"Now would to God," said the King, "that they were all three here!"

"That shall never be," said Lancelot, "for two of them shall ye never more see. But one of them shall come again."

HOW SIR GALAHAD SAW THE HOLY GRAIL

AFTER leaving Sir Lancelot, Galahad rode many journeys in vain. Wherever he went, strange signs and marvels followed, but not yet did he behold the vision of the Holy Grail.

It befell on a day that as he rode out of a great forest he was overtaken by Sir Percival, who had followed him for five days, and just afterwards at a cross-road they met Sir Bors. There is no need to tell if they were glad. They told each other their adventures, and all rode on together.

Thus they travelled a great while, till they came to the same Castle of King Pelles where Sir Lancelot had already been, and directly they entered within the Castle King Pelles knew them. Then there was great joy, for all the people knew well by their coming that they had fulfilled the Quest of the Holy Grail.

A little before evening when they were gathered in the hall, a voice was heard among them, and it said, "They that ought not to sit at the table of Jesus Christ arise, for now shall true knights be fed." So everyone went away save King Pelles and Eliazar his son who were holy men, and a maid who was his niece; these three and the three knights were left, no more.

Soon they saw nine knights, all armed, come in at the hall door, and take off their helms and their armor.

"Sir," they said to Galahad, "we have hied right much to be with you at this table, where the holy meat shall be parted."

Then said he, "Ye be welcome, but from whence come ye?"

Three of them said they were from Gaul, and another three said they were from Ireland, and the other three said they were from Denmark.

Then a voice said, "There are two among you who are not in the Quest of the Holy Grail; therefore let them depart." So King Pelles and his son departed.

The knights who remained now saw the table of silver, whereon was the Holy Grail, and it seemed to them that angels stood about it, and it seemed a service was being held. They set themselves at the table in great dread, and began to pray. Then came One, as it seemed to them, in the likeness of the Lord Christ, and He said:

"My knights, and my servants, and my true children, which are come out of deadly life into spiritual life. I will no longer hide Me from you, but ye shall see now a part of My secrets, and My hid things; now hold and receive the high meat which ye have so much desired." Then He Himself took the holy vessel, and came to Galahad, who knelt down and received the sacred food, and after him, in like manner, all his companions received it; and they thought it so sweet it was marvellous to tell.

Then said He to Galahad, "Son, knowest thou what I hold between My hands?"

"Nay," said he, "unless Thou wilt tell me."

"This is," said He, "the holy dish wherein I ate the lamb at the Last Supper. And now hast thou seen that which thou most desired to see, but ye hast not seen it so openly as thou shalt see it in the city of Sarras, in the spiritual place.

Therefore thou must go hence and bear with thee this holy vessel, for this night it shall depart from the realm of Logris, and shall never more be seen here. And wouldst thou know wherefore? Because these of this land are turned to evil living, therefore I shall disinherit them of the honor which I have done them. Therefore, go ye three tomorrow to the sea, where ye shall find your ship ready,—you and Sir Percival, and Sir Bors, and no more with you. And two of you shall die in My service, but one of you shall go back again to Camelot, and bear the tidings."

Then He blessed them and vanished from their sight.

So Galahad, Percival, and Bors left the Castle of King Pelles. After riding three days they came to the seashore, where they found the same ship in which Galahad had stayed with Lancelot; and when they went on board they saw in the midst the table of silver, and the Holy Grail, which was covered with red samite. Then were they glad to have such things in their fellowship.

So they sailed away, till they came to the city of Sarras, where they landed, taking with them the table of silver. As they went in at the gate of the city, they saw sitting there a crooked old man, and Galahad called to him and bade him help them carry the heavy table.

"Truly," said the old man, "for ten years I have not walked, except with crutches."

"Never mind," said Galahad, "arise up, and show thy goodwill."

The old man tried to rise, and immediately found himself as whole as ever he had been. Then he ran to the table and took the side opposite Galahad.

The fame of this cure went through the city, and when the King of the City saw the three knights, he asked them whence they came, and what thing it was they had brought upon the table of silver. They told him the truth of the Holy Grail, and the power God had placed in it to cure sick people.

The King, however, was a tyrant, and came of a line of pagans, and he took the three knights, and put them into prison, in a deep dungeon. But all the time they were in prison they were supported by the holy grace of heaven.

At a year's end it came to pass that the King lay sick, and felt that he should die. Then he sent for the three knights, and when they came before him he begged mercy of them for all that he had done to them, and they willingly forgave him, and so he died.

When the King was dead all the city was dismayed, and knew not who could be their King. Right so, as they were in council came a voice among them, and bade them choose the youngest knight of the three to be their King. So they made Galahad King, with the assent of the whole city.

When he had surveyed the country, Galahad caused to be built round the table of silver a chest of gold and of precious stones, which covered the holy vessel, and every morning early the three knights would come before it and say their prayers.

Now at the year's end, on the very day that Galahad was given the crown of gold, he arose up early, he and his companions, and came to the palace, to the holy vessel. There they saw before them a man kneeling, in the likeness of a bishop; and round about him was a great fellowship of angels.

"Come forth, Galahad, servant of Jesus Christ," he said, "and thou shalt see that which thou hast long desired to see."

Then Galahad began to tremble, for a vision of spiritual

things rose before his earthly eyes; and holding up his hands to heaven, he said:

"Lord, I thank Thee, for now I see that which hath been my desire many a day. Now, blessed Lord, I would not longer live, if it might please Thee, Lord."

Then the good man took the holy food, and proffered it to Galahad, and he received it right gladly and meekly.

When this was done, Galahad went to Sir Percival and Sir Bors, and kissed them, and commended them to God. And to Sir Bors he said, "Fair lord, salute me to my lord, Sir Lancelot, my father, and as soon as ye see him, bid him be mindful of this unstable world."

Afterwards he knelt down before the table, and said his prayers, and suddenly his soul departed to Jesus Christ.

Then it seemed to the two knights that there came a hand from heaven, and bore away the holy vessel. And since that time there was never any man so bold as to say he had seen the Holy Grail.

When Percival and Bors saw Galahad dead they made as much sorrow as ever did two men, and if they had not been good men they might easily have fallen into despair. And the people of the city and the country were right heavy. As soon as Galahad was buried Sir Percival retired to a hermitage, and here for a year and two months he lived a full holy life, and then he passed away.

Sir Bors stayed always with Sir Percival as long as he lived, but when he was dead Sir Bors took ship and went back to the realm of Logris, and so came to Camelot, where King Arthur was. Great joy was made of him in the Court, for they all thought he must be dead, because he had been so long out of the country. Sir Bors told them all the adventures of the Holy Grail, and to Sir Lancelot he gave Galahad's message.

"Sir Lancelot," he said, "Galahad prayeth you to be mindful of this uncertain world, as ye promised him when ye were together more than half a year."

"That is true," said Lancelot. "Now I trust to God his prayer shall avail me."

THE DEATH OF ARTHUR

THE DEPARTING OF SIR LANCELOT

AFTER the Quest of the Holy Grail had been fulfilled and all the knights that were left living were come again to the Round Table, then there was great joy at Court, and in especial King Arthur and Queen Guinevere rejoiced, and were passing glad because of Sir Lancelot and Sir Bors. And for a time all went well, and there was much feasting and gaiety.

But Sir Lancelot forgot his promise to the good hermit to see as little as possible of Queen Guinevere, and because he was held in such high favor by the King and Queen and all the people, some of the other knights were jealous of him, and tried to do him all the mischief they could.

Among the knights at King Arthur's Court, the most spiteful and malicious was Sir Mordred. He was the youngest son of King Arthur's sister, the wife of King Lot of Orkney, and it was to him that Merlin referred when he prophesied that a child born on May Day should bring destruction to King Arthur. He was half-brother to the noble knights Gawaine, Gaheris, and Gareth, but nothing at all like them in disposition. The only brother who in the least resembled him was Sir Agravaine, and it was owing to the evil-speaking of these two malicious knights that the storm of anger and misfortune arose, which never ceased till the flower of chivalry of all the world was destroyed and slain.

In the pleasant month of May, when every noble heart glows with life,—when earth is looking her sweetest and brightest, and all men and women rejoice and are glad because summer is coming with freshest flowers,—in the beautiful month of May, these two knights, Agravaine and Mordred, set their mischief on foot. In open assembly before many knights they told slanderous tales of Sir Lancelot and Queen Guinevere, and suggested that these should be repeated to the King. Then spoke Sir Gawaine:

"Brother Sir Agravaine," he said, "I pray you and charge you, speak no more of such things before me, for wit ye well, I will not be of your counsel."

"Truly," said Sir Gaheris and Sir Gareth, "we will have nothing to do with your deeds."

"Then I will," said Mordred.

"I well believe that," said Sir Gawaine, "for always, if there is any mischief you will be share in it, brother Sir Mordred: I wish you would leave this, and not make yourself such a busy-body, for I know what will come of it."

"Come of it what come may," said Sir Agravaine, "I shall speak to the King."

"Not by my counsel," said Sir Gawaine, "for if there arise war and wreck between Sir Lancelot and us, wit you well, brother, many Kings and great lords will hold with Sir Lancelot. As for my part I will never be against Sir Lancelot, when he rescued me from King Carados of the Dolorous Tower, and slew him, and saved my life. Also, brother Agravaine and Mordred, in like wise Sir Lancelot rescued you both, and three score knights, from Sir Turquine. It seems to me that such good deeds and kindness should be remembered."

"Do as you like," said Sir Agravaine, "for I will hide it no longer."

At that moment King Arthur came near.

"Now, brother, stay your noise," said Gawaine.

"We will not," said Agravaine and Mordred.

"Will you not?" said Gawaine; "then God speed you, for I will not hear your tales, nor be of your counsel."

"No more will I," said Sir Gareth and Sir Gaheris, "for we will never speak evil of that man."

And accordingly these three knights left the assembly.

"Alas," said Gawaine and Gareth, "now is this realm wholly put in mischief, and the noble fellowship of the Round Table is dispersed."

So, very sorrowfully, they went their way.

King Arthur coming up at that moment asked what the noise was about, whereupon Agravaine and Mordred were only too ready to repeat their spiteful slander. As the King would scarcely believe what they said, they laid a plot to entrap Sir Lancelot. In escaping from this ambush, Sir Lancelot slew Sir Agravaine and twelve of his companions. Sir Mordred managed to escape, and riding all wounded and bleeding to the King, told him his own version of the story.

"Alas!" said King Arthur, "I sorely repent that ever Sir Lancelot should be against me. Now I am sure the noble fellowship of the Round Table is broken for ever, for with him will hold many a noble knight."

It all fell out as the King and Sir Gawaine had foreseen. From that day there was constant fighting in England, some knights taking part with Sir Lancelot and some with the King, and on both sides many gallant lives were lost. Through sad mischance, the noble knights Sir Gaheris and Sir Gareth, who were unarmed at the time, were accidently slain by Lancelot's party, after which Sir Gawaine, who had hitherto refused to fight against him, became his most bitter enemy. Many a time the King and Sir Lancelot would have made peace, but it was always Sir Gawaine who urged the King on to fresh fighting, and persuaded him not to listen to any attempts at conciliation, although Sir Lancelot made the most noble offers of penitence, and expressed the deepest sorrow for the unintentional slaying of Gaheris and Gareth.

At last the Pope sent a command that the fighting should cease, and a stately meeting between the King and Sir Lancelot took place at Carlisle. Here Sir Lancelot spoke such noble words that all the knights and ladies who were present wept to hear him, and the tears fell down King Arthur's cheeks. But the King, to gratify Gawaine's revenge for the loss of his brothers, had already promised that Lancelot should be banished, and now instead of accepting his offer of penitence and good-will, he allowed Sir Gawaine to declare to Sir Lancelot his doom of exile, and that he was forbidden to abide in England more than fifteen days.

Then Sir Lancelot sighed, and the tears fell down his cheeks.

"Alas, most noble Christian realm," he said, "whom I have loved above all other realms, in thee have I gotten a great part of my honor, and now I shall depart in this wise! Truly, I repent that ever I came into this realm, that am thus shamefully banished, undeserved and without cause! But fortune is so variant, and the wheel so movable, there is no constant abiding, and that may be proved by many old chronicles, of noble Hector, and Troilus, and Alexander the mighty conqueror, and many others more. When they were highest in their royalty they alighted lowest, and so it fareth with me," said Sir Lancelot, "for in this realm I had honor, and by me and the Knights of my blood the whole Round Table increased more in renown than by any other."

Then Sir Lancelot bade good-bye to Queen Guinevere in hearing of the King and them all.

"Madam," he said, "now I must depart from you and this noble fellowship forever, and since it is so, I beseech you to pray for me, and say me well. And if you be hard bested by any false tongues, my lady, have word sent to me, and if any knight's hands can deliver you by battle, I shall deliver you."

And therewith Sir Lancelot kissed the Queen, and then he said all openly:

"Now let us see any one in this place that dare say the Queen is not true to my lord Arthur! Let us see who will speak, if he dare speak!"

With that he brought the Queen to the King, and then Sir Lancelot took his leave and departed. And there was neither King, duke nor earl, baron or knight, lady or gentlewoman, but all of them wept as people out of their minds, except Sir Gawaine. And when the noble Sir Lancelot took his horse to ride out of Carlisle, there was sobbing and weeping for pure sorrow at his departing. So he took his way to his Castle of Joyous Gard, and ever after that he called it the Dolorous Gard.

And thus departed Sir Lancelot from the Court of King Arthur forever.

When Sir Lancelot came to Joyous Gard he called his company of knights together, and asked them what they would do. They answered all together with one voice that they would do as he did.

"My fair fellows," said Sir Lancelot, "I must depart out of

this most noble realm, and how I shall depart it grieveth me sore, for I shall depart with no honor. For a banished man never departed out of any realm with any honor, and that is my cause of grief, for ever I fear after many days they will chronicle of me that I was banished out of this land."

Then spoke many noble knights, and said:

"Sir, if you are so disposed to abide in this country we will never fail you, and if you do not choose to abide in this land, not one of the good knights here will fail you. Since it pleased us to take part with your distress and heaviness in this realm, wit you well, it shall equally please us to go into other countries with you, and there to take such part as you do."

"My fair lords," said Lancelot, "I well understand you, and as I can thank you. And you shall understand that such livelihood as I am born to, I will give up to you in this manner,—namely, I will share all my livelihood and all my lands freely among you, and I myself will have as little as any of you; and I trust to God to maintain you on my lands as well as ever were maintained any knights."

Then spoke all the knights at once:

"Shame on him that will leave you! For we all understand that in this realm will now be no quiet, but always strife and debate, now the fellowship of the Round Table is broken. For by the noble fellowship of the Round Table was King Arthur upborne, and by their nobleness the King and all his realm were in quiet and in rest. And a great part, everyone said, was because of your nobleness."

"Truly," said Sir Lancelot, "I thank you all for your good words, though I know well all the stability of this realm was not due to me. But as far as I could I did my duty, and some rebellions in my days were appeased by me. And I trow we shall soon hear of them again, and that is what grieves me sorely. For ever I dread me that Sir Mordred will make trouble, for he is passing envious, and applies himself to mischief."

So all the knights were agreed to go with Sir Lancelot, and quite a hundred departed with him, and made their vows they would never leave him, for weal or woe.

So they shipped at Cardiff, and sailed to Bayonne, in France, where Sir Lancelot was lord of many lands.

THE VENGEANCE OF SIR GAWAINE

NOT content with having banished Sir Lancelot, King Arthur and Sir Gawaine made a great host ready, and prepared to follow him, taking ship at Cardiff. During his absence King Arthur appointed his nephew Sir Mordred to be chief ruler of all England, and put Queen Guinevere under his charge. So he passed over the sea and landed on Sir Lancelot's lands, and there, through the vengeance of Sir Gawaine, he burned and wasted all that they could overrun.

When word was brought to Sir Lancelot that King Arthur and Sir Gawaine were landed and destroying all his possessions, his knights urged him to go forth to battle, but he replied that he was full loath to ride out to shed Christian blood, so first he would send a message to King Arthur, to see if a treaty could be made, for peace was always better than war. So Lancelot sent forth a damsel to King Arthur, demanding that he should cease warring against his lands.

The damsel started on her palfrey, and when she came to the pavilion of King Arthur she alighted; and there met her a gentle knight, Sir Lucan the butler.

"Fair damsel, do you come from Sir Lancelot of the Lake?"

"Yea, sir," she said, "I come hither to speak with my lord the King."

"Alas," said Sir Lucan, "my lord would love Lancelot, but

Sir Gawaine will not let him." And then he added, "I pray to God, damsel, ye may speed well, for all we that are about the King would that Sir Lancelot did best of any knight living."

With this Lucan led the damsel to King Arthur, where he sat with Sir Gawaine, to hear what she would say. When she had told her tale, tears filled the King's eyes, and all the lords were full glad to advise the King to be reconciled with Sir Lancelot, save only Sir Gawaine.

"My lord, my uncle, what will you do?" he said. "Will you turn back again, now that you have come thus far on this journey? All the world will speak scorn of you."

"Nay," said King Arthur, "you know well, Sir Gawaine, I will do as you advise me; and yet it seems to me it were not good to refuse his fair proffers. But since I am come so far upon this journey, I will that you give the damsel her answer, for I cannot speak to her for pity, her proffers are so generous."

Then Sir Gawaine said to the damsel thus:

"Damsel, say you to Sir Lancelot, that it is waste labor now to sue to my uncle. For tell him if he would have made any attempt at peace, he should have made it before this time, for tell him now it is too late. And say that I, Sir Gawaine, so send him word that I promise him by the faith I owe to God and to knighthood, I shall never leave Sir Lancelot till he have slain me, or I him."

So the damsel wept and departed, and there were many weeping eyes. She came back to Sir Lancelot, where he was among all his knights, and when Sir Lancelot heard this answer, then the tears ran down his cheeks.

Then his noble knights strode about him, and said, "Sir Lancelot, wherefore make you such cheer? Think what you are, and what men we are, and let us noble men match them in midst of the field."

"That may easily be done," said Lancelot, "but I was never so loath to do battle, for I will always avoid that noble King who made me knight. When I can keep quiet no longer, I must needs defend myself, and that will be more honor for me, and for us all, than to strive with that noble King whom we have all served."

Then they spoke no more, and as it was night, went to rest.

On the morrow early, in the dawning of the day, as the knights looked out, they saw the city of Bayonne besieged round about, and ladders were fast being set up. Then from the town they defied King Arthur's host and beat them from the walls mightily. So the siege went on for six months, and there was much slaughter of people on both sides. Then it befell on a day that Sir Gawaine came before the gates, armed at all points, on a noble horse, with a great spear in his hand.

"Where art thou now, thou false traitor, Sir Lancelot?" he cried with a loud voice. "Why hidest thou thyself within holes and walls, like a coward? Look out, now, thou false traitor knight, and here I shall revenge upon thy body the death of my three brethren."

Every word of this was heard by Sir Lancelot, and all his knights, and now there was nothing to be done but for Sir Lancelot to defend himself, or else to be recreant forever. Sir Lancelot bade saddle his strongest horse, and fetch his arms, and bring them all to the gate of the tower, and then he spoke aloud to King Arthur:

"My lord Arthur, and noble King who made me knight, wit you well I am right heavy for your sake that you pursue

me thus, and always I forbear you, for if I had been re-
vengeful, I might have met you in open field, there to have
made your boldest knights full tame. Now I have forborne
half a year, and suffered you and Sir Gawaine to do what
you would do, and now I can endure it no longer,—now I
must needs defend myself, inasmuch as Sir Gawaine hath
accused me of treason. It is greatly against my will that
ever I should fight against any of your blood. But now I
cannot resist it, I am driven to it, as a beast to bay."

"Sir Lancelot," cried Gawaine, "if thou darest do battle,
leave thy babbling, and come away, and let us ease our
hearts."

King Arthur's host outside the city stood still, all apart, and
Lancelot's noble knights came out in a great number, insomuch that when King Arthur saw the multitude of men and
knights he marvelled, and said to himself:

"Alas, that ever Sir Lancelot was against me, for now I
see he hath borne with me!"

So the covenant was made that no man should go near
Lancelot and Gawaine, or have anything to do with them,
till the one was dead or yielden.

Now, years ago, a holy man had given a strange gift and
favor to Sir Gawaine, which no one knew of except King
Arthur. Every day in the year, from nine o'clock in the morning till high noon, his might increased three times its usual
strength. The King appointed most trials of arms to take
place at this time of day, which caused Sir Gawaine to win
great honor.

Thus Sir Lancelot fought with Sir Gawaine, and when he
felt his strength evermore increase, Lancelot wondered, and
sorely dreaded to be shamed. But when it was past noon Sir
Gawaine had nothing but his own strength to rely on, and

then Lancelot felt him grow weaker. Then he doubled his strokes, and gave Sir Gawaine such a buffet on the helm that he fell down on his side, and Lancelot withdrew himself from him.

"Why withdrawest thou?" said Sir Gawaine. "Now turn again, false traitor knight, and slay me. For if thou leave me thus, when I am whole I shall do battle with thee again."

"I shall endure you, sir, by God's grace," replied Sir Lancelot, "but wit you well, Sir Gawaine, I will never smite a felled knight."

So Sir Lancelot went back into the city, and Sir Gawaine was borne into one of King Arthur's pavilions, where doctors came to him and dressed his wounds.

Then King Arthur fell sick for sorrow because Sir Gawaine was so sorely hurt, and because of the war betwixt him and Sir Lancelot. Those of King Arthur's party kept the siege with little fighting outside, and those within guarded their walls and defended them when need was.

Sir Gawaine lay sick in his tent for about three weeks, and as soon as he could ride he once more came before the chief gate of Bayonne, and challenged Lancelot to fight. And once more Lancelot wounded him sorely and smote him down.

"Traitor knight," cried Sir Gawaine, "wit thou well, I am not yet slain; come thou near me, and perform this battle to the uttermost."

"I will do no more than I have done," said Sir Lancelot; "for when I see you on foot, I will do battle against you all the while I see you stand on your feet; but to smite a wounded man that cannot stand, God defend me from such shame!" And then he turned, and went his way towards the city.

"Sir Lancelot, when I am whole, I shall do battle with

thee again," Sir Gawaine called out after him, "for I shall never leave thee till one of us be slain."

So the siege went on, and Sir Gawaine lay sick nearly a month. And when he was well recovered and ready within three days to do battle again with Sir Lancelot, tidings came to King Arthur from England, which made the King and all his host remove.

THE BATTLE IN THE WEST

WHILE King Arthur was away in France, Mordred, who had been appointed ruler of England, was busy about his own wicked plots. He now forged letters, as though they came from beyond the sea, and the letters specified that King Arthur had been slain in battle with Sir Lancelot. Mordred thereupon summoned a Parliament, and calling the lords together, he made them choose him King; so he was crowned at Canterbury, and held a feast there fifteen days. Afterwards he withdrew to Camelot, and sent for Queen Guinevere, and told her plainly that he wished to marry her. Everything was made ready for the feast, and the day for the wedding was fixed.

Queen Guinevere was in great distress, but she did not dare oppose Sir Cordred openly, and therefore she pretended to agree. Then she asked leave to go to London, to buy all manner of things necessary for the wedding. Because of her fair words Sir Mordred trusted her well enough and gave her leave to go.

Directly she reached London, Queen Guinevere at once seized the Tower, and in all haste possible stuffed it with all manner of victuals, and well garrisoned it with men and so kept it.

When Mordred found he had been out-witted he was wroth beyond measure. He went and laid a mighty siege to the Tower of London, and assaulted it with great engines

312

and guns, but he could not prevail. He tried in all ways, by letters and messages, to make Queen Guinevere come out of the Tower, but it availed nothing; neither for fair words nor foul would the Queen trust herself again in the traitor's hands. She answered shortly that she would rather slay herself than marry him.

Then word came to Mordred that King Arthur had raised the siege on Sir Lancelot, and was coming homeward with a great host to be avenged on his nephew. Mordred accordingly sent writs to all the baronry of England, and numbers of people flocked to him. For it was a common report among them that with Arthur was no other life but war and strife, and with Mordred was great joy and bliss. Thus was King Arthur maligned, and evil spoken of. And there were many whom King Arthur had raised up from nothing, and given lands to, who could not now say of him a good word.

So Sir Mordred marched with a large host to Dover, and there came King Arthur with a great navy of ships and galleys, while Mordred waited ready to prevent his landing. Then there was launching of big boats and small, full of noble men of arms, and there was much slaughter of gentle knights, and many a bold baron on both sides was laid low. But King Arthur was so courageous, no manner of men could prevent his landing, and his knights fiercely followed him. They drove Mordred back, and he fled, and all his army.

After the battle was over, King Arthur buried his people that were slain, and then the noble knight Sir Gawaine was found in a boat, lying more than half dead. He had been hurt again on the wound which Sir Lancelot had given him at Bayonne, and now he must die.

"Alas, Sir Gawaine," said the King, "here now thou liest,

the man in the world whom I loved the most, and now is my joy gone! In Sir Lancelot and thee I had most joy, and now have I lost you both."

"Mine uncle, King Arthur," said Gawaine, "wit you well, my death day is come, and all is through my own hastiness and wilfulness. Had Sir Lancelot been with you as he used to be, this unhappy war had never begun, and of all this am I the cause. For Sir Lancelot and his kindred through their prowess held all your enemies in subjection and danger, and now ye shall miss Sir Lancelot. But alas, I would not agree with him, and therefore I pray you let me have paper, pen and ink, that I may write to Sir Lancelot a letter with my own hand."

Then Sir Gawaine wrote a letter to Sir Lancelot, "flower of all noble knights," telling him all that had happened, and how he had brought his death on himself, because he was hurt on the same wound that Lancelot had given him at Bayonne.

"Also, Sir Lancelot," he went on, "for all the love that ever was betwixt us, make no tarrying, but come over the sea in all haste, that thou mayst with thy gallant knights rescue the noble King who made thee knight, that is my lord Arthur, for he is full straitly bested with a false traitor, my half-brother, Sir Mordred."

Then Sir Gawaine bade King Arthur send for Lancelot, and cherish him above all other knights; and so, at the hour of noon, Sir Gawaine yielded up the spirit.

After this, King Arthur fought again with Sir Mordred, and drove him westward across England, towards Salisbury, where a day was appointed for the King to meet Sir Mordred in battle on a down near Salisbury, not far from the sea.

The night before the battle King Arthur dreamed a wonderful dream. It seemed to him he sat on a platform, in a chair, clad in the richest cloth of gold that could be made; and the chair was fast to a wheel. And the King thought that under him, far from him, was a hideous deep black water, and therein were all manner of serpents and worms, and wild beasts, foul and horrible. And suddenly, the King thought, the wheel turned upside down, and he fell among the serpents, and every beast seized him by a limb.

Then the King cried as he lay in his bed—"Help!" And knights, squires, and yeomen ran to the King and wakened him, and he was so amazed he did not know where he was.

Then he feel slumbering again, not sleeping, nor thoroughly wakening. And it seemed to him that Sir Gawaine came to him, and warned him not to fight with Sir Mordred on the morrow, for if he did so he would certainly die. Sir Gawaine counselled him to make a treaty for a month, for within that time Sir Lancelot would come, with all his noble knights, and would rescue King Arthur, and slay Sir Mordred.

Then Sir Gawaine vanished.

Directly King Arthur awoke he sent for all his wise lords and bishops, and told them his vision, and of Sir Gawaine's warning. They went at once to Sir Mordred, and made a treaty, promising him that while King Arthur lived he should have Cornwall and Kent, and after the King's death, the whole of England. It was further agreed that a meeting between King Arthur and Mordred should take place betwixt the two armies, and each of them should take fourteen persons.

King Arthur, on starting for this meeting, warned all his army that if they saw any sword drawn they were to come on fiercely, and slay the traitor Mordred, for he in no wise trusted him. And in like manner Sir Mordred also warned his host.

So they met, as had been appointed, and they were agreed and thoroughly in accordance. Wine was fetched, and they drank.

Just as that moment came an adder out of a little heath-bush, and it stung a knight on the foot. When the knight felt himself stung, he looked down, and saw the adder. Then he drew his sword to slay the adder, and thought of no other harm.

But when the host on both sides saw that sword drawn, then they blew bugles, and trumpets and horns, and shouted grimly. So both the armies rushed to arms, and never was seen a more doleful battle in any Christian land.

All that day long they fought without ceasing, and when night came, of all King Arthur's noble knights there were none left alive but Sir Lucan the butler, and his brother Sir Bedivere, and both were sorely wounded. Then was King Arthur wroth out of measure when he saw his people so slain from him.

"Alas, that ever I should see this doleful day! For now I am come to my end," said Arthur. "But would to God I knew where that traitor Sir Mordred is, who hath caused all this mischief."

Then was King Arthur aware where Sir Mordred leaned on his sword among a great heap of dead men. Sir Lucan tried to persuade the King not to fight with Mordred, reminding him of Sir Gawaine's warning.

"Blessed be God, ye have won the field," he said; "for here we are three alive, and with Sir Mordred there are none living. And if you leave off now, this wicked day of destiny is past."

"Tide me death, betide me life," said the King, "now I see him yonder alone, he shall never escape my hands, for at a better advantage I shall never have him."

"God speed you well!" said Sir Bedivere.

Then King Arthur took his spear in both hands, and ran towards Mordred, crying:

"Traitor, now is thy death day come!"

When Sir Mordred heard King Arthur he ran at him with his sword drawn. Then King Arthur thrust Mordred through the body with his spear, so that he fell dead; but Mordred's sword pierced the helmet and brain-pan of King Arthur, so that he fell in a swoon to the earth.

"THE NOBLEST KNIGHT OF THE WORLD"

Sir Lucan and Sir Bedivere lifted up King Arthur and carried him to a little chapel not far from the seashore, but Sir Lucan was so grievously wounded that he fell dead before they could go to a further place of safety. Sir Bedivere wept for the death of his brother, but the King bade him stay his mourning, for his own life was hurrying fast away.

"Therefore," said Arthur, "take thou Excalibur, my good sword, and go with it to yonder water-side; and when thou gettest there I charge thee throw my sword in that water, and come again, and tell me what thou there seest."

"My lord," said Bedivere, "your commandment shall be done, and I will quickly bring you word again."

So Bedivere departed, and by the way he beheld that noble sword, how that the pommel and the hilt were all of precious stones. Then he said to himself, "If I throw this rich sword in the water, good will never come of it, but harm and loss."

So Sir Bedivere hid Excalibur under a tree, and went back to the King as quickly as he could, and said he had been at the water, and thrown in the sword.

"What saw thou there?" said the King.

"Sir," he said, "I saw nothing but waves and winds."

"That is untruly said," spoke the King. "Therefore go thou quickly again, and do my command as thou art lief and dear to me; spare not, but throw it in."

Then Bedivere went back and took the sword in his hand; and then it seemed a sin and shame to throw away that noble sword; so again he hid the sword, and returned to Arthur, and told him he had done his command.

"What saw thou there?" said the King.

"Sir," he said, "I saw nothing but the ripple of water, and the lapping of the waves."

"Ah, traitor, untrue!" cried King Arthur, "now hast thou betrayed me twice. Who would have thought that thou who hast been to me so lief and dear, and thou wert named a noble knight, would betray me for the riches of the sword! But now go again quickly, for thy long tarrying putteth me in great jeopardy of my life."

Then Sir Bedivere departed, and fetched the sword, and taking it to the water-side, he bound the girdle about the hilt, and threw the sword as far into the water as he could. There came an arm and a hand above the water, and met it, and caught it, and so shook it thrice and brandished it, and then the hand with the sword vanished away in the water. So Sir Bedivere came again to the King, and told him what he had seen.

"Alas," said the King, "help me hence, for I dread me I have tarried over long."

Then Sir Bedivere took the King upon his back, and so carried him to the water-side. And when they reached it, a barge drifted in quite close to the bank, with many fair ladies in it; they had all black hoods, and they wept and cried when they saw King Arthur.

"Now put me into the barge," said the King, and Sir Bedivere did so softly.

And there received him three Queens, with great mourning, and so they set him down, and King Arthur laid his

319

head in the lap of one of the Queens.

"Ah, dear brother," she said, "why have ye tarried so long from me?"

Thus, then, they rowed from the land, and Sir Bedivere beheld them go from him.

"Ah, my lord Arthur," he cried, "what shall become of me now ye go from me, and leave me here alone among my enemies?"

"Comfort thyself," said the King, "and do as well as thou canst, for in me is no trust to trust in. For I go to the vale of Avalon, to heal me of my grievous wound. And if thou hear never more of me, pray for my soul."

Thus King Arthur was borne away in the barge with the three Queens,—the one was King Arthur's sister, Morgan le Fay, another was the Queen of North Wales, the third was the Queen of the Waste Lands. Also in the barge was Vivien, the chief Lady of the Lake, and this lady had done much for King Arthur.

And some people say that King Arthur died, and that the three Queens took his body to a little hermitage near Glastonbury, where it was buried in a chapel. But many men think that King Arthur never died at all, but dwells now in some beautiful valley of rest, and that one day he will come again to rule over England. For on his tomb this verse is written:

"Here lies Arthur, King that was, and King that shall be."

When news came to Queen Guinevere that King Arthur was slain, and all the noble knights, and Sir Mordred, she stole away with five ladies to Amesbury. There she took refuge in a convent, and spent the rest of her days in fasting, prayers, and alms-deeds.

In the meanwhile, Sir Lancelot had received Sir Gawaine's

letter, and with all the haste he could he hurried back to England with his company of noble knights. But when they arrived they found they were too late, King Arthur and Sir Mordred were both slain. Sir Lancelot thereupon rode in search of Queen Guinevere, and at last he found her in the nunnery at Amesbury. The Queen told him that she intended never to come out again into the world, and when Lancelot heard this, he determined also to retire to a hermitage.

Taking his horse he rode away into a great forest, and so it chanced he came to the little chapel near Glastonbury, where the body of King Arthur had been buried. Sir Bedivere was still there, and Sir Lancelot asked the good bishop who was hermit, if he might remain. Here Sir Bors followed him, and others of his noble knights, who when they found Sir Lancelot had betaken himself to such holiness, had no desire to depart. Thus for six years they lived a life of penance, paying no regard to worldly riches, and caring nothing what pain they endured, when they saw the noblest knight of the world suffer such hardship.

Sir Lancelot had lived in the hermitage about seven years when one night a vision came to him, bidding him hasten to Amesbury, for there he would find Queen Guinevere dead. And Lancelot was told to take a horse-bier, and go with his fellow knights to fetch the body of Queen Guinevere, and bury her by her husband, the noble King Arthur.

So all was done as the vision commanded, and Queen Guinevere was brought from Amesbury to Glastonbury with much sorrow and splendor. A hundred torches were kept burning round the bier, and Lancelot and seven of his knights walked always round it, singing, and saying holy prayers, and strewing frankincense. Thus they came from Amesbury to Glastonbury, and on the morrow Queen Guinevere was buried in the little chapel, in the tomb of King Arthur.

When the coffin was put into the earth Sir Lancelot swooned, and lay for a long time still, till the good Bishop, who was hermit, came out and awaked him.

"Ye be to blame," he said, "for ye displease God with such manner of sorrow making."

"Truly," said Sir Lancelot, "I trust I do not displease God, for he knoweth my intent. My sorrow was not, and is not, from any sinful cause, but my sorrow can never have an end. For when I remember the beauty of the Queen, and the nobleness that was with her and the King,—and when I saw them thus lie here together dead,—truly my heart would not serve to sustain me. Also, when I remember me, how by my fault, my arrogance, and my pride, they were both laid full low, who were peerless of any Christian people, wit you well," said Sir Lancelot, "this remembrance of their kindness and my unkindness sank so to my heart, that I could not sustain myself."

After this, Sir Lancelot fell ill, eating and drinking little, and gradually pining away, for there was nothing anyone could do to comfort him. Evermore, day and night he prayed, but sometimes he slumbered a broken sleep, and often he was found lying on the tomb of King Arthur and Queen Guinevere. At last he grew so weak that he could no longer rise from bed, and then he sent for the good Bishop and all his faithful companions, and begged that he might receive the last sacred rites of religion. When all had been done in due order, he prayed the Bishop that when he was dead his comrades might bear his body to his own Castle of Joyous Gard, for there he had sworn a vow he would be buried.

Then there was weeping and wringing of hands among

his fellow knights.

That night, while all lay asleep, the good Bishop had a beautiful dream. He thought he saw Sir Lancelot surrounded with a great throng of angels, and they carried him up to heaven, and the gates of heaven were opened to him.

"It is but a dream," said Sir Bors. "I doubt not nothing but good aileth Sir Lancelot."

"That may well be," said the Bishop. "But go ye to his bed, and then we shall know the truth."

When Sir Bors and the other knights came to Sir Lancelot's bed, they found him stark dead, and he lay as if he smiled, and all around him there was the sweetest fragrance that ever they felt.

On the morrow, after chanting the Requiem Mass, the Bishop and the knights put Sir Lancelot in the same horse-bier in which Queen Guinevere had been brought to Glastonbury, and took him to his own Castle of Joyous Gard, and they had always a hundred torches burning about him; and so within fifteen days they came to Joyous Gard. There they laid him in the body of the choir, and sang and read many prayers and psalms over him; and his face was left uncovered, that all folk might see him, for such was the custom in those days.

And right thus, as they were at their service, came Sir Ector de Maris, who for seven years had sought all England, Scotland, and Wales for his brother Lancelot. When he heard the noise, and saw the choir of Joyous Gard all lighted up, he dismounted from his horse, and came into the choir, and there he saw men singing and weeping. And they all knew Sir Ector, but he did not know them. Then Sir Bors went to Sir Ector, and told him how there lay his brother, Sir Lancelot, dead. Sir Ector threw his shield, sword, and helm from him, and when he beheld Sir Lancelot's face, it were hard for any tongue to tell the doleful complaints that he made for his brother.

"Ah, Lancelot," he said, "thou wert head of all Christian knights. And now, I dare say," said Sir Ector, "thou, Sir Lancelot, there thou liest, that thou wert never matched of earthly knight's hand; and thou wert the courtliest knight that ever bare shield; and thou wert the truest friend to thy lover that ever bestrode horse; and thou wert the truest lover of any sinful man that ever loved woman; and thou wert the kindliest man that ever struck with sword; and thou wert the goodliest person that ever came among press of knights; and thou wert the meekest man and the gentlest that ever ate in hall among ladies; and thou wert the sternest knight to thy mortal foe that ever put spear in the rest."

Then there was weeping and grief out of measure.

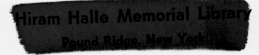